How to Survive Your Computer Workstation

JULIA S. LACEY

WITH TOM DICKSON, DC, CN

AND HOWARD LEVENSON, OD

Sharon Simkin

Hoping you find our work readable, useful, enjoyable. Thanks for waiting!

CRT Services, Inc.

Julia Lacey

11/6/95

A CRT Services, Inc. Publication
Post Office Box 1525
Kerrville, Texas 78029
1-800 256-4379

First printing 1990
Second printing, revised and updated 1994

ISBN 09623-656-01

Illustrations by Ellen Stratton
Revised edition designed by Carol Haralson

Printed in Canada

To Mother,
who taught her
children to ask,
"Why?"

. . . and
to the memory of
my Gran,
Julia Selby Lombard Bryant.

"I always wondered what became of you," said Tanya. . . .

"I work in a company that makes computers," she said. "I get to test them at the final stage, before the customer gets them. It's hell on my eyes, but the company's gotten so many complaints from workers like me I hope they'll soon do something about it; make screens or something to put in front of the computers, or design special eyewear."

ALICE WALKER, *The Temple of My Familiar*

ACKNOWLEDGMENTS

Raymond Hartley went every step of the way with me, installing anti-glare filters, repositioning monitors, and compiling questionnaires. His competence and reliability made this book possible.

For the steadfastness of a dozen readers, many of whom read and made suggestions to three revisions of my work, I am grateful. Because of their generous help, my work became publishable.

I'm grateful for the special efforts of my Aunt Selby, Mrs. James H. Stratton, who pushed and prodded and propped me up for three long years. I'm equally grateful to my twin brother Jimmy Lacey who, when it really mattered — early on—took pen in hand to edit copy, giving the manuscript life and spurring me on to further thought, writing, and editing.

Dr. Marion Ellis gave patiently and generously of his telephone time; Dr. Joe Sweere went over the entire manuscript with a fine-toothed comb; Dr. Tom Dickson read and reread the Physical section and contributed to the Stress section; and Dr. Howard Levenson made a careful reading of and corrections to the Visual section. To each of them I am endebted.

I extend my deepest gratitude to Sylva Billue of the Syvenna Foundation, which assists women writers. Her unflagging friendship and support brought this project to bear fruit.

Rick Barry exibited unusual kindness and generosity when he took me, a total stranger, by the hand, sat me down in his office, and proceeded, in spite of his heavy schedule, to advise me on how I could bring you a better book — this edition.

I'm touched by and thankful to my youngest brother Doug Lacey for his undying friendship, understanding, and assistance.

Likewise, I'm humbled by and ever grateful for the guidance and assistance of my lifetime friend and mentor, Audrey Withers Kennett.

Contents

III STRESS

RESOURCES

FOREWORD

TOM DICKSON, DC, CN
Dickson Chiropractic, Winston-Salem, N.C.

This book is long overdue. It contains information that can help relieve the stress and suffering of millions who spend their days at computer terminals. The problems of computer workers are very real but often unrecognized by management and — worse — by the workers themselves.

Occupations that entail full-time, long-term work at computer terminals are among the most stressful and demanding in the world, both physically and emotionally. They also require special, though little celebrated, physical and visual capabilities.

Who should be a full-time CRT worker? If you are selecting, or have already taken, an occupation in the computer world, you should consider your physical, visual, and emotional makeup and how they will withstand the demands of the job.

Backache, neckache, depression, and excessive fatigue are only a few of the warning signs of job stress that too many computer users exhibit.

We know that a good computer operator fares better with a positive attitude, a body that can withstand hours of physical punishment, eyes with strong lateral and vertical coordination, and an ability to maintain a sense of calm under pressure, all while concentrating on enormous loads of data. By any standards, that's a pretty tall order.

Let's look at four other things needed to do your job well: The right work environment, good posture, good physical structure, and proper nutrition.

Look at Marilou, someone employers consider the average

worker. Since Marilou began working full time at a computer for a mail-order house, she has been having some problems. She wonders why she has developed headaches, worse all the time, and why her neck aches, her legs have developed varicose veins, her thighs are gaining girth, and her back stings at night. She doesn't know she is drifting toward spinal degeneration, arthritis, and eventual lower-than-standard productivity.

Because this "average worker" doesn't fit the equipment she is using, her condition is primarily caused by postural fatigue. The height of her chair, the distance of her eyes from her terminal, and the relationship of her shoulders to her keyboard were all set by "averages"— industry averages. Possibly one in 100 of her co-workers fits correctly and comfortably at this desk — the one who has no complaints, of course.

But Marilou is not average, and neither are most of us. Contrasted with dimensions required for "fitting" her workstation, she may be too tall from waist to shoulder, too long of leg, too thick of hand. Even her breast development may be causing excessive shoulder strain. She, her employer, and the industry that produces computer equipment must explore better ways to meet the needs of the majority of people who don't fit the average mold.

Next, consider posture. Your posture, on and off the job, can be an asset, or a hindrance, to your long- and short-term performance and health.

Many women have problems such as those of Wilma, a woman in her forties whose creeping weight gain in midriff and thighs has had a pulling effect on her back muscles, and has caused a swayback effect on her lumbar vertebrae similar to what she experienced during the last three weeks of her several previous pregnancies.Wilma is a victim of another natural enemy of the full-time sitter: rounded shoulders. Shoulder muscles are designed to hold our necks and heads erect, to hold our shoulder blades upright so our arms can fall freely, and to keep our thoracic spines gently rounded so our rib cages can expand and contract gently with each easy breath.

Breathing difficulties can further complicate matters. Optimum posture minimizes breathing difficulties so that when we breathe deeply oxygen rushes through our blood, feeding our cells, ridding our systems of the toxins of cell metabolism, and minimizing the cause of muscle stiffness and aching joints.

Where does your spine fit into the picture? Well, the key to good posture is a healthy spine — *your* healthy spine — the development of which is remarkable indeed. As a baby you entered the world in the fetal position, with your spine curved like the letter *C*. Your first major spinal task was to strengthen your muscles so that you could hold up your head — which you probably did by your fourth or fifth month of life. And by doing this you formed the first curve in your spine, the curve within your cervical vertebrae.

The second major change in your spinal development occurred when you were about a year old. With an ever-strengthening lower back and abdominal muscles and with great persistence, you finally stood erect. The result was a spine that from the side now looks a bit like the letter *S*. The curves in your spine will be with you for life and are essential to painless and optimum body mobility.

Occasionally, unfortunately, life batters the youngster's developing spine. Serious injury may occur, as it did to Sally, a highly skilled CRT operator with serious health problems. She aches every day, hates her job, and constantly fights depression.

She doesn't know that her problem began at age eleven, when she fell from a horse, broke her arm, and began to suffer from an undetected strain in her neck and lower back.

Sally's arm healed. All seemed well until, when she was twenty-one, her car was hit from the rear, tearing her ligaments and muscles, stretching her discs, and pinching the nerves in her spine. She took no notice beyond treating the symptoms by swallowing pain relievers.

She doesn't know that her spine is bruised and beaten, that it has lost the cervical curve it developed at the age of four months, that it has developed a lateral curve (called scoliosis) in an attempt to compensate for her constant backache.

Unfortunately, Sally is probably no candidate for full-time work at a computer workstation. Treatment can help, but it cannot cure physical problems like Sally's.

Finally, there's the problem I call the sugar roller-coaster. Consider Nan, a young computer operator, frequently over-tired, the victim of her own junk-food diet.

She starts the day without breakfast, then makes up by midmorning snacking on office doughnuts and cakes — "just a bit." For her body to assimilate these "short-chain" sugars, it draws down on her vital storage of B-complex vitamins. Instead of fresh fruit and vegetables and lean protein, she turns to quick-processed foods — pizza, hot dogs, deep-fried chicken, processed meats, prepackaged entrees — and canned (versus fresh or frozen) vegetables. Her choices add chemical stress to her system while failing to fully replace lost nutrients. She thinks she makes up for whatever she has missed by drinking milk — after all, isn't it the perfect food for babies? (In fact, over 60% of adults in America have allergies to milk. Allergies can cause bloating, headache, and fatigue.)

Nan has secured herself a seat on the sugar roller coaster. She has a nutritional problem that has reached epidemic proportions in America. When she grabs a candy bar to fight fatigue, her body quickly absorbs the simple sugars, elevating her blood sugar rapidly and triggering insulin production by her pancreas. The insulin causes her cells to absorb the sugar rapidly and her blood sugar level to drop abruptly. The highs and lows hit her brain in violent waves that exhaust her adrenal system as it tries valiantly to normalize the sugar lows by stimulating the production of blood sugar from muscle storage. No wonder Nan is tired most of the time.

But Nan has a choice: She can eat a diet rich in fiber and the complex carbohydrates that come from fruit, pasta, potatoes, rice, and good bread, plus a sufficiency of protein. She can jump off the sugar roller coaster and stay off it forever.

In conclusion, the examples cited above, and throughout this book, cover what we now know is essential for your success and health as a full-time worker at a computer terminal.

Julia Lacey and I have long discussed a number of the solutions described herein and the need for this book. Indeed, she first came to me for a regular monthly adjustment during which time the question arose, "Wouldn't regular monthly adjustments be a reasonable step for the computer user to take?"

As a chiropractor, I heartily agreed, though at the time I could hardly have imagined the great breadth with which Ms. Lacey would approach her subject in this book.

I find it admirable that she makes no medical or other pretensions. She has developed her techniques over time, refining them based on her own experience and that of the individuals she has helped. Her work continues. You, the reader, can add to the knowledge that will help others by experimenting with the information in this book and sending the results of your CRT-User Wellness Survey back to the author.

In closing, let me challenge you to become increasingly aware of problems that face computer workers and to become a partner in helping to find solutions, for yourself and for others.

INTRODUCTION

Howard Levenson, OD
Marin Optometric Group, San Rafael, CA.

Each day, approximately 75 million Americans[1] sit down to work before glaring television-type monitors. Whether travel agents, word processors, medical technologists, insurance clerks, or home computer users, all share a common bond: Life in a technological age in which the video display terminal and the keyboard link users to computers that have revolutionized how America works.

These computer operators share other characteristics, but they have received little publicity. They include backache, eyestrain, aches and pains in limbs, and stress. Consequently, absenteeism has increased, turnover is high, and productivity — the foremost reason people use computers — is not what it could be.

This is the other side of computer America.

Why has this occurred? Because employers and employees have been slow to realize that a computer terminal is nothing but another office tool. As with any tool, a cathode-ray tube (or CRT, also called a video display terminal or VDT)[2] must be used properly if we are to obtain maximum benefit from it while at the same time preventing injury from it.

Other nations, particularly Japan and the countries of Western Europe and Scandinavia, have been quick to realize that working at CRTs is different from working at typewriters and drafting tables. Many nations have enacted guidelines for office use of CRTs. In countries with such guidelines worker complaints seem less frequent and less serious than in our own country, particularly with regard to visual problems.

In the United States, some cities and states have begun to enact standards for CRT use in offices. Until the problems are understood, however, laws are not likely to effect real solutions to computer-user problems.

This book tells how employers and employees can work together to alleviate most, if not all, of the stresses and ills associated with CRT work. These guidelines for beneficial CRT use are based upon the author's thousands of hours of field research and experience as a consultant in the setup and use of CRTs. Using common sense and her own years of office experience, the author has isolated a number of ways to combat and prevent the physical problems afflicting CRT users.

Major universities, both here and abroad, have completed scientific studies on CRTs and ergonomics — how people can best use these marvelous tools. Until recently, however, scientists' knowledge has not been augmented by practical field experience.

Computers are expensive. But hiring, training, and keeping good employees are also expensive. And so are absenteeism, turnover, and medical insurance claims.

The information in this book can save employers and employees more than just money. It can turn CRT workplaces into healthy, productive environments where absenteeism and medical claims are rare. Best of all, many of the suggested guidelines cost nothing to implement.

Some of these tips for CRT operators may seem contradictory. Can eye fatigue really be reduced by pushing the monitor farther from the worker's eyes? In most cases, the answer, surprisingly, is Yes.

Some suggestions are contrary to long-accepted company practices. For instance, CRT workers need shorter but more frequent breaks to rejuvenate their eyes and bodies. When frequently refreshed, they feel better and are more productive. Attendance records improve and medical claims decrease.

Employers who test these suggestions will be pleasantly rewarded by their salutary effect. CRT operators who use these techniques will be much healthier and happier.

The computer revolution will continue. The ranks of CRT users will grow by millions every year. CRT users and their employers can continue to use outdated approaches to a new technology — or they can decide to cut the revolution's casualties and be healthier and more productive.

The choice is simple.

[1]Number of monitors as of January 1, 1993, according to Lloyd Cohen of International Data Corporation in Framingham, Massachusetts. Mr. Cohen's statistics indicate the existence of about 60 million personal computers (PCs) and 15 million terminals connected to multi-user systems in the United States. He believes that the bulk of these 75 million terminals are in the workplace.

[2]Monitors are variously called cathode ray tubes (CRTs), video display terminals (VDTs) and video display units (VDUs). The breakdown is, respectively, among users, academia, and Western Europe. As this book is written for computer users, and as they comprise the majority of the 75 million terminals tallied by International Data Corporation, I have decided to refer to the TV-type monitor set atop the users' desks as a CRT. I also identify CRTs as monitors, displays, and terminals.

PREFACE

JULIA S. LACEY
Computer Workstation Health Consultant

I have had considerable success in eliminating the pain, discomfort, and fatigue associated with sitting in awkward, unnatural positions when working many hours at a CRT workstation.

I do not pretend to recognize organic injury, much less do I pretend to recognize disease. This is not a medical book, and I am not a medically trained person.

Furthermore, the results of my work have been so effective that if none of the suggestions alleviates worker pain, discomfort, and absenteeism — whether or not you associate your difficulty with CRT work — I urge you to make an appointment with a physician.

Be warned. Time and again you will read that I suggest assuming certain postures and holding them while working. A knowledgable person knows that static work — work accomplished through no *apparent* physical effort — is unlikely to be effective. I agree. You should never hold the positions I recommend for more than five or ten minutes. I suggest these positions knowing you will realize the importance of taking to heart the suggestions of the book as a whole: Good posture, deep breathing, eye exercises, rest breaks, a stroll at noon and in the evening.

If you take my advice about workstation posture, set up your workstation wisely, *and* take regular productivity breaks throughout the day, you will work better, feel better, and protect both your physical health and your mental well-being.

I have tried to make desk exercises reasonably discreet.

Nonetheless, I hope you will feel free to move about as much as possible while seated. Movement is *essential* to minimizing physical discomfort.

USING THIS BOOK

This book is written both for future and current users of CRTs. The first three major sections of the book — Physical, Visual, and Stress — are devoted to specific user problems within those categories. Each of these sections is divided into six segments, the first two of which are introductory. The third segment of each is written for the person who has not yet set up a workstation. The fourth segment is written for the person who already is working at a workstation and has troubles because the workstation was set up by conventional standards. The fifth segment emphasizes a major concept for optimizing health and comfort. The sixth and final segment is a form designed to help you resolve a widespread problem pertaining to that section.

The Resources section at the end of the book is devoted to products and publications of value to CRT users. The information includes general price ranges and sources.

THE WELLNESS SURVEY©

Following this introduction is the CRT-User Wellness Survey©, developed and refined over several years in my effort to catalogue and resolve CRT user work-related problems.

If you are already a CRT user, please fill out this form. The survey lays the groundwork for getting the most from this book. Its purpose is to help you identify the frequency and severity of the difficulties you face as a CRT worker. This in turn will tell you where in the book to place emphasis for problem solving.

After you have filled out the survey, please read the entire book through once. Your body is an entity, no one part of which is unrelated to any other part. Difficulties tend to overlap. And so it is with CRT user problems: Headache, eyestrain, and stress, for instance, all compound one another, and it can be difficult indeed to know wherein lies the cause. In reading the entire book, you will see how your difficulties relate to one another, and have a greater chance of pinpointing the cause of your trouble. After you have read the book through, review your CRT-User Wellness Survey© and, based on this review, turn next to the section of the book which seems most related to optimizing workstation comfort for you.

• Fill out the CRT-User Wellness Survey©.

• Read the book through, without stopping to work out any problem.

• Return to your survey for analyzing your difficulties.

• Then move on to the section that seems most pertinent to resolving your problems.

I wish you all the best in your effort, and have every confidence you will soon leave your workstation rested at day's end.

CRT-USER WELLNESS SURVEY©

Following is the CRT-User Wellness Survey© I developed for analyzing CRT-User problems and needs. I have identified the most common workstation difficulties. You may experience problems not listed. Please note any of these in the appropriate area, or attach an extra sheet of paper. I encourage you to elaborate on any matter. Your feedback will help others. I'd be particularly pleased to know of any special solutions you've developed.

Here is the scoring system for filling in the survey.

FREQUENCY		SEVERITY	
0	None	0	None
1	Rarely	1	Hardly noticeable
2	Occasionally	2	Noticeable
3	Frequently	3	Uncomfortable
4	Most of the time	4	Distracting/I leave my desk when possible
		5	I would or do leave work for home if possible

Note that I ask you to fill out the survey on three different occasions. This allows you to assess conditions, make needed changes, reassess, and so on. Having completed the survey the second time, you should catch any lingering problems. Finally, the third run at the survey should reveal that you have pretty well optimized work conditions at your workstation. Those of you who like to quantify situations can do so using the subtotal and grand total blocks.

Numerous CRT users experience no trouble while working at a monitor. If you happen to be one of these people and you're just reading this book to make your workstation more comfortable, please provide that response. Statistically, your response is important and essential. Even if your response is "no problems" I need this information.

Please provide your name and social security number for use as sorting tools. All names will be held in strictest confidence. At a later date, CRT Services will be contacting some of you who have provided more novel solutions.

So, if you also gave me your telephone number, I could call you to discuss any unusual topics covered on your CRT-User Wellness Survey©.

It is easier working from a photocopy of the survey sheet. Try this if you have access to a copier. Further, using a photocopy of the survey will allow you to reuse it as often as you like and to make copies for others.

Your information is critical to the effort of compiling information and creating solutions. I'll be very grateful to those of you who return the completed survey to me. It will become your contribution to helping others like yourself.

Send surveys and comments to:

CRT Services, Inc.
Post Office Box 1525
Kerrville, Texas 78029

Thanks for your help.

CRT USER WELLNESS SURVEY©

Name____
Address____
Clty__________________State____________Zip__________

	DAY 1		DAY 2		DAY 3	
DATE:	/ /		/ /		/ /	
PHYSICAL	F*	S*	F*	S*	F*	S*
Headache						
Neckache						
Backache						
Middle back						
Lower back						
Shoulder ache						
Arms, tired						
Wrists, ache						
Hands, ache						
Fingers, tired, tingling						
Legs, discomfort						
Feet, tingling						
Toes, numbness						
S/TOTAL						

	DAY 1		DAY 2		DAY 3	
VISUAL	F*	S*	F*	S*	F*	S*
Blurred Vision						
Burning eyes						
Watery eyes						
Dry eyes						
Itchy eyes						
Eyeball ache (entire)						
Front of eye						
Back of eye						
Eyestrain						
Floaters						
Redness						
Pink aftereffect						
S/TOTAL						

	DAY 1		DAY 2		DAY 3	
STRESS-RELATED	F*	S*	F*	S*	F*	S*
Boredom						
Fatigue						
Depression						
Stress						
Irritability						
Insomnia						
Other						
S/TOTAL						
GRAND TOTAL						

F = Frequency of occurrence

S = Severity

See the chart on page 28.

PHYSICAL

The Workstation and Physical Problems

Ergonomics, the science of designing workplaces, equipment, and jobs to fit the capabilities and limitations of workers, has shown that poor workplace design and bad work habits are counterproductive and costly. Ergonomics has made great strides in many industries; yet this is not true for the computer workstation, a relatively new work setup, but an employer of about 75 million workers in the United States alone.

A major problem with computer work is that it can keep an operator at a workstation all day. Why? Because all the books that used to stand on shelves and all the files that used to be in file cabinets are now scrolling in front of our eyes.

A second major problem: CRT users are presumed to be lowering their productivity when not at their monitors. Nothing could be further from the truth; yet users are generally disciplined for excess time away from the terminal.

A third major problem is workstation design. Many workstations force computer users to sit in awkward positions.

Sitting absolutely still all day at a desk is an entirely new development in the history of business. Among office workers, the primary cause of back pain is sitting — lack of physical exercise, lack of physical variation, lack of even the slightest movement. More force is exerted on the spine during sitting than standing.

Within 90 seconds of sitting, incorrect pressure is exerted on spinal discs.

Sitting unflinchingly exacerbates the problem of sitting itself, causing discomfort in general and increasing back pain. An awkward position at the workstation can result in other problems: Headache and neckache, for instance.

These problems do more than cause pain and discomfort. They decrease accuracy, productivity, and morale. Health costs have soared over the past decade and claims rates continue to surge.

What can be done to stop these problems?

Plenty!

Let's start by looking at a general guide to good CRT-user health.

The CRT User's Guide to Good Health

Keep in mind that pain and discomfort are the body's way of telling you something is wrong, that damage may be occurring. If you are effectively safeguarding the body against pain and discomfort, you are likely preventing damage too.

First and foremost, sitting at a workstation all day is a new work condition and can take its toll on computer operator health. It won't surprise you that lack of comfort, with its resulting aches and pains, lowers productivity and increases the frequency of insurance claims. These results cost *you* more than they cost your company.

In the pages that follow, we will examine the stumbling blocks that challenge the natural efficiency of our bodies and see how the removal of those obstacles promotes comfort, thereby maximizing productivity.

Time and again, I suggest assuming certain positions, and *holding* these positions while working. However, let me make clear that you should *never* hold these positions for more than five or 10 minutes at a time. The positions are suggested for providing maximum comfort over the long term. But they can only work when coupled with regular, intermittent breaks built into your schedule.

Thus, you can assume these positions and hold them while working at your monitor, but you still must break regularly — four or five times per hour — and do appropriate exercises at your desk. In addition, you can take a brisk 10-minute walk at noon and a vigorous 20- to 30-minute walk after you get home. Then you will be taking my advice *as a whole,* which is what is intended.

It is my best advice that for the first three hours of CRT work you move physically away from your workstation *every 30 minutes* and not return for one or two full minutes. As the day progresses, if you are still doing CRT work, you should have a break of two or three minutes every 30 minutes. This point will be reemphasized throughout the book. It is very important.

Note that exercises are well-rounded, and — if you include vigorous walks — they maximize movement of all parts of your body.

Repeatedly, I recommend three solutions in particular for most physical problems, in spite of the vast differences in symptoms.

First, I recommend workstation design based on *your* analysis of *your* physique, *your* physical requirements, and the problems you are experiencing at *your* workstation.

Second, I strongly recommend postures for working, sitting, and standing that prevent, by day's end, the symptoms of physical stress.

Third, I strongly recommend frequent breaks away from your workstation. You must accept the fact that the body was never intended for static (i.e., still) vs. dynamic (i.e., moving) work.

Every study on the human body reinforces this concept. You will be healthy and pain-free only if you move about at your workstation and get away routinely for work productivity breaks.

The following guidelines help prevent problems caused by poorly set up workstations. However, remember that good workstation design and regular exercise are suggested in addition to — not instead of — an annual medical examination. If you have been having aches and pains at your workstation, *only* a proper medical exam can ascertain the presence of organic problems.

MAJOR ELEMENTS OF PHYSICAL PROBLEMS

Computer operators who spend at least half the day at their workstation tell me they experience headache, neckache, and backache. An alarming number report problems with their legs.

The most important step in eliminating all physical problems is getting physically away from your workstation every half hour. When working long days at my monitor, I back off from my workstation every 10 or 15 minutes. This is easy to do for two reasons: I have a stand-up workstation (which position particularly suits my physical needs); and I am my own boss. You should make certain that you can at least lean back in your chair and stretch every five or 10 minutes, no matter what your work conditions. It takes only five or six seconds to lean back, stretch, and roll your shoulders. The major elements of CRT-user *physical* problems are:

- **physical variation;**
- **placement of the monitor;**
- **placement of the keyboard;**
- **height of the desk; and,**
- **fit of the chair.**

Using a workstation that does not fit your physiological dimensions causes problems, most of which are addressed in the following section. Essentially, eliminating physical problems entails setting up your workstation correctly and moving about at your workstation and away from it.

PHYSICAL VARIATION

Both moving about *at* your workstation and getting physically *away* from it are extremely important. This major concept underlies each section (PHYSICAL, VISUAL and STRESS) of this book. Adequate physical variation is the underpinning of good physical health, whether at your workstation or at home. In order for all the cells of your body to receive nutrients and oxygen, blood must flow through your body. Exercise enhances circulation.

PLACEMENT OF THE MONITOR

The monitor must be set at *about* eye level. Studies indicate people enjoy looking somewhat down when reading, and this notion has been carried over to the workstation. I quite agree with it. But placing the monitor too low causes neck muscles to be used in a constant pattern of lifting and lowering the head.

In working with CRT operators I help the user determine where, on some level *just* below eye level, the user is most comfortable reading the monitor. This position depends a lot, of course, on the distance between the user's eyes and the monitor. The greater the distance, the greater the angle tolerated. For example, if the monitor is four feet from the user's eyes, it can be 20 to 25 degrees below eye level. If it is only two feet away, it will need to be only five to 10 degrees below eye level.

PLACEMENT OF THE KEYBOARD

When the keyboard is placed just below the hands, where the elbow forms a 90-degree angle between shoulder and hand, and if part of the hand can gently touch a support, the neck and shoulder muscles work minimally.

HEIGHT OF THE DESK

Desk height should allow for the keyboard to force a 90-degree angle, more or less, at the elbow. Adjustments can be made. Raise the desk by adding supports to the legs, or effectively lower it by placing the keyboard on an open desk drawer. Of course, if you own the desk, you may shorten its legs!

FIT OF THE CHAIR

An ill-fitting chair can wreck any workstation. This is important enough that I have constructed a format for choosing a chair — see the Chair Evaluation Form© at the end of this section. On the other hand, the body is not meant to sit all day, much less as rigidly as is dictated by CRT work. So a good chair, though it can prevent a lot of back pain, should not be construed as taking the place of movement, work breaks, and exercise.

Now let's look at solving some problems that arise when these elements are not taken into consideration.

SPECIFIC PHYSICAL PROBLEMS AND THEIR SOLUTIONS

Results of my CRT-User Wellness Survey© shows 67% of full time VDT users reporting headache, 48% reporting neckache, and 29% reporting both backache and shoulder ache. Not an easy way to get a day's work done.

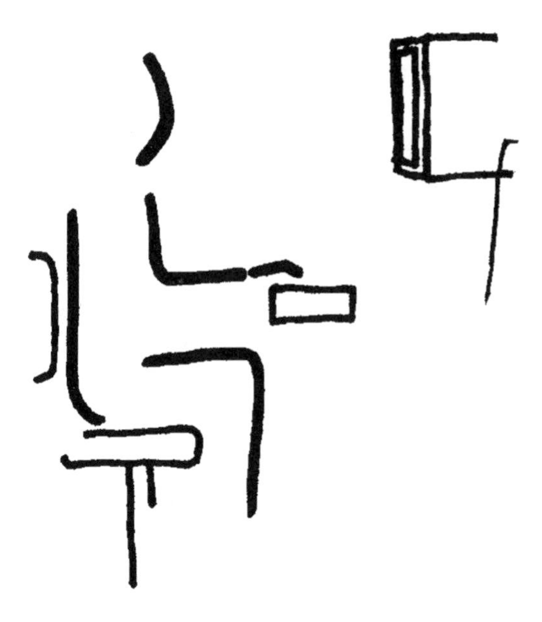

Through examination of the workstation and a series of questions put to the CRT user, I was successful in eliminating 100% of these problems. Success entailed customizing the workstation. That is what you will have to do for yourself. Through careful reading of the solutions to your problems and application of the following guidelines, you, too, should be able to work in comfort, in spite of the number of hours spent at your computer. An estimated 70% of CRT work time is spent in one position, and holding that one position too long is the major cause of discomfort and pain.

Keep in mind that if you had some chronic condition *before* taking your computer job and it has become only more intense with computer work, setting up your workstation correctly might be helpful, but it won't take the place of a proper medical examination. You are advised to set priorities regarding your health.

The importance of seeing a doctor for any constant, nagging pain — occurring before, during, or after you take on computer work — cannot be overemphasized.

The following guidelines will take you from the top of your head down to your toes — an order that, curiously, approximately reflects the order of frequency of computer operator complaints.

HEADACHE

Amazing, but nine of 10 CRT users who work at video display terminals more than four hours a day report experiencing headache and neckache. Yet most headache and neckache, as well as most workstation problems, can be prevented by implementing simple, usually cost-free measures.

The major causes of headache are:

- **the monitor's brightness, and**
- **tension and stress.**

Working at your monitor all day is like staring at a light bulb all day. The brighter the light, the more you squint, and the keener your discomfort and headache.

Eliminate your discomfort by:

- **installing an anti-glare filter, and**
- **adjusting down the brightness of your monitor.**

It is usually very important to use an anti-glare filter. My opinion was reinforced by my experience of using a particular screen, an "inside-mounted" mesh filter. My success in helping CRT users with such a product led to my study of CRT-user problems in general.

When you have finished this book, read about the anti-glare filter in the Resources section.

✔ BRIGHTNESS HEADACHES

Screen brightness is a matter of personal preference. It should be based on what *your* eyes see and how they react to brightness. No matter how bright you set your monitor, it should be the brightest object in the room. This does not mean that your monitor should be bright — only that it should be the brightest light in the room. Thus, overall room lighting should be lower than in the standard office setting to ease eyestrain.

To lower room brightness:

- **replace overhead fluorescent tubes with individual desk or reading lamps, if possible;**
- **remove about half the overhead fluorescent tubes, if you can't replace them;**
- **replace overhead lamp bulbs with about half the wattage in use.**

> *Caution: Don't reduce the screen brightness too much. This can cause you to strain to read the monitor. I always tell CRT operators I work with to dim the monitor's light to the point at which it feels they are straining a bit to read, then to turn it up.*

I find that dimming the monitor's light too much, then slowly turning it back up, is the most effective way to adjust brightness. Stop just at the point at which you can read the monitor. Try this brightness for five minutes. If you feel you are squinting or straining, turn the light up just a bit more.

✔ TENSION HEADACHES

Fighting screen brightness and general office pressures can cause neck stress and shoulder tension which lead to headache.

Eliminate stress by using:

- **full, deep breathing**
- **neck and shoulder exercises**
- **short but frequent breaks of one or two minutes away from your workstation, during which you breathe deeply .**

When you feel a tension headache coming on, get up and walk away from your workstation.

- ***Leave* the workstation.**
- **Take a two-minute stroll.**
- **Breathe very deeply for the full two minutes. Feel your chest expanding as you breathe in. Hold each breath. Exhale.**
- **Stretch.**
- **Roll your neck and shoulders round.**
- **Go back to your work only after two full minutes.**

✔ FRONTAL HEADACHES

Frontal headache spans the front surface of the head. The cause is often eyebrow muscle tension from fighting glare and screen brightness. Eliminate glare by repositioning the monitor away from sources which reflect off it and by reducing screen brightness. (See "Optimizing Visual Health and Comfort: Glare".)

Frontal headache can also indicate visual problems. More on this is included in the next major section, VISUAL. If adjusting for excessive brightness does not solve your problem, make an appointment for an eye examination.

✔ HEADACHES SURROUNDING ONE EYE

Headache surrounding one eye may result from working at a monitor that isn't positioned directly in front of your eyes. If the monitor is off center, it can cause the eye nearest it to work harder than the other eye. Check your monitor position for "squareness." If your monitor *is* squared with your eyes, headache surrounding one eye can result from having one eye which is weaker or more sensitive to light than the other, in which case pulling the screen the slightest bit closer to the weaker eye can relieve stress on it. See more on this in the VISUAL section.

✔OTHER HEADACHES

Any number of causes provoke headache, of course, and others are covered in the VISUAL section. Improper neck posture and movements also can lead to headache.

NECKACHE

The major causes of neckache are:

- **poor posture;**
- **the position of the monitor;**
- **not using a reference material stand, or using one improperly; and,**
- **improper style of eye glasses.**

✔WORKSTATION POSTURE

The cause of most neckaches is poor workstation posture coupled with an incorrectly positioned monitor. Neckache, however, can be completely eliminated by good workstation posture and correct monitor placement.

Good sitting posture means holding the head up, the chin slightly up, and the shoulders up and back. Remember, *no* sitting position is perfect over the long term — the spine simply wasn't meant to sit for excessively long periods without relief, so it's difficult to call any sitting position "correct." That is why I refer time and again to "good" or "optimum" workstation posture — to emphasize that particular postures can minimize discomfort.

✔POSITION OF THE MONITOR

Keeping your head upright allows your muscles to support your surprisingly heavy head in a manner least taxing to your entire spine.

> *Consider that your head weighs 10-15 pounds! When your head is balanced atop your spine, your neck muscles do not have to strain to hold it up.*

When working at your CRT, arrange the keyboard so that your arms form a right angle (90 degrees) at the elbows. If you lean forward too far, your shoulder muscles must tense up to support your arms. This shoulder tension can transfer right up the spine, becoming neckache.

Neck and shoulder exercises are very helpful in preventing neckache. Just roll your neck and shoulders from side to side, up and down, several times *every* half-hour. Take advantage of "response time" and "down time." Use these periods to take deep breaths and roll your neck and shoulders around.

✔REFERENCE MATERIAL STAND

"Hmmm . . . let's see, now . . . hmmm . . . Where was I?"

How many times a day have you said that? How many times a day do you still say that?

For CRT operators who also must answer telephones, trying to "find one's place" is an endless frustration.

> *Improper placement of monitor and reading materials can double or triple the number of neck movements required during the day. Use the "let your eyes do the walking" concept instead.*

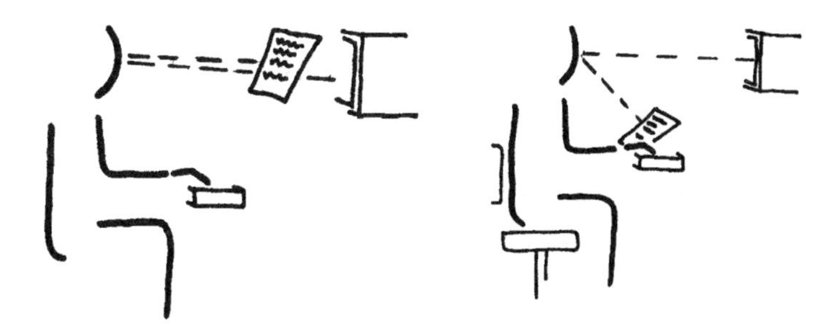

The constant neck craning and head dipping brought on by trying to read reference papers which lie flat on your desktop can cause terrible neckache. This can be eliminated completely by proper use of a reference-material stand.

Unless you can rearrange your desk creatively, a reference material stand (copy holder) is essential to exercising and maintaining *good* posture. Lack of a copy holder is the second most common cause of neckache. (The first is positioning a monitor too far below eye level.) Incorrect placement of a copy holder can also cause neckache.

No matter what kind of computer work you do (entering data, retrieving data, or answering the telephone while doing word processing), you need a copy holder. In short, if you work at a monitor more than 15 minutes a day, you need a copy holder to protect your cervical (upper) vertebrae and your sanity, and to be efficient. If your boss doesn't understand the value of a copy holder but you like him and your job, spend your own money for one, and don't complain about having done so. The loss of good mental health costs you more than the lost productivity costs your boss.

You'll be happy indeed to learn the crick in your neck does not come with the job, and that it has gone forever. A copy holder costs $10-100, depending on the number of breakable parts. See the Resources section.

Placement of the copy stand is critical. It should be placed:

- **about the same height (on the same horizontal) as your monitor.**
- **near the monitor's side; and,**
- **about the same distance from the eye as the monitor.**

The fulltime computer operator makes an estimated *30,000* head, neck, and shoulder movements daily. The above guideline should eliminate at least one-third, and possibly half, of those movements. Placing the holder about eye level relieves the neck muscles of picking the head up and letting it down. Placing the holder near the monitor relieves the neck muscles of the constant left and right movement. And equal distance from the eye makes for minimal refocusing of the eye muscles.

By the way, if you frequently find yourself trying to reestablish correct finger contact with the keyboard, paint clear nail polish into the cup of the "J" key. This will allow repositioning by touch rather than through the frequent neck-craning required by looking down.

✔ EYEGLASSES

Old-style bifocals, whether having a half-moon inset or a division running completely across the lenses, can cause neckache. Such glasses call for constant craning of the neck to see first near, then afar. These glasses are designed for reading at about 15 or 18 inches.

If you wear bifocals while using your monitor, or if you have considered getting the drugstore variety, reconsider. See your eye doctor for *full lenses focused at CRT distance.* These are not the same as glasses designed for standard reading distance. Read more on this topic in the Visual section.

SHOULDER ACHE

The way you hold your shoulders and use your arms at your workstation directly affects your level of comfort while at work, and for the first hour or two after leaving work.

Poor posture — in this case, using the arms inefficiently — can create aches and pains in other parts of your body. *Remember, no part of your body is isolated from the other parts. You are one.*

As the severity of aches and pain increases, discomfort creeps into nearby areas.

Consider your arms as 10 to 20 pound weights attached to your shoulders. If you hold them out from you, reaching to your keyboard, your shoulders will quickly tire. But if your upper arms fall to your sides and your desk height and keyboard are adjusted to fit your lower arms, your shoulders will rarely complain.

Factors which affect shoulder ache are:

- **the position of your arms;**
- **the height of your desktop;**
- **the position of your keyboard;**
- **lack of physical variation.**

✔ARM POSITION

First, assume good posture, sitting or standing. Let your arms fall to your sides. Sense how your upper back feels. Now extend your arms in front of you as if you were holding a book and reading. As you extend your arms, feel how this causes your neck, shoulder, and upper arm muscles to tense. Feel the struggle involved in fighting the gravity which is pulling your arms to the ground.

This rule of gravity also applies, of course, if you hold your arms in front of you while keying.

To find the optimal position, let your arms drop straight

down by your sides. Now raise your hands to the keyboard, forming an L shape, a 90-degree angle, at your elbow. Slowly alternate the correct and incorrect position several times. Feel the immediate relief each time you reach the correct position.

This arm position is very restful to the shoulders and back, thereby helping prevent shoulder ache by day's end. Remember good posture: Sit up straight and hold your shoulders back. Slumping — "rounded shoulders" — can cause aches and pains in your shoulders and upper back, and can provoke discomfort and exhaustion throughout your entire body.

✔DESKTOP HEIGHT

Checking your desk for correct height will be easier with the help of an office mate.

- **Remove your keyboard from the desk.**
- **Sit erect in your chair.**
- **Hang your arms to your sides.**
- **Assume keying position, an "L" at the elbow.**
- **Have your office mate locate where your outside elbow bends.**
- **Measure down an inch or two.**

This level, about two inches below your elbow, is approximately the best desk height for you. This two-inch space is where the keyboard fits. Here's how to adjust desk height:

- **UP: Many European desks have adjustable legs. If yours does not, obtain four identically sized blocks and place one under each leg.**

- **TILT: Placing blocks under the desk's two back legs will lower the front slightly and give a tilt to the desk resembling that of a drafting table. This tilt can be very pleasant if you do some writing throughout the day.**

• DOWN: If the desktop is too high, you can effectively raise your desk by putting a small platform under your chair. (If the desk is yours — if you paid for it — you're free to size down the legs as necessary.)

✔ DESKS FOR MOUSE USERS

As you now know, the arrangement of furniture may contribute to any number of discomforts and injuries. What is the impact on users of the now omnipresent "mouse"?

Bevi Chagnon, president of PubCom, a publishing consultants firm in Takoma Park, Maryland, and an instructor in graphic design at George Washington University in Washington, D.C., has found that people using a mouse tend to lean too far forward while rolling the mouse across their desktops or mouse pads. As one spending too many uninterrupted hours at a monitor, she has found — and verified among others — that leaning too far forward for extensive periods of time can cause neck, back, shoulder, and arm fatigue and pain. This would apply, of course, to desktop publishers, designers, word processors, artists, clerks — anyone using a mouse.

Ms. Chagnon has observed that when users arrange their desks in an L-shape, their "mouse arms" are able to rest more naturally by their sides on a desktop area placed perpendicular to the main desk area where the keyboard is located. Consequently, they are less likely to lean forward, instead sitting straighter and more comfortably during long work sessions. She cautions that users must make sure they sit close enough to the mouse so that they don't lean sideways to operate it. "Tuck yourself into the L so that your desk supports your arm naturally, but not overly so," she advises.

KEYBOARD POSITION

For you to maintain the arm position shown above, the keyboard must lie directly below the hands. The fleshy outside of the palm may rest on the leading edge of your keyboard, or on the flat desktop between you and the keyboard.

> *Caution: When keying, you generally do not want your lower arm to lie flat on the desk. If your arms lie flat on the desk and your hands are raised for keying, you force an angle to occur at the wrist — an angle known to cause wrist problems. (There is more on this under Wrists.)*

✔ IMPORTANCE OF PHYSICAL VARIATION

Remember that your body must move if you are to prevent tension and soreness. Roll your shoulders forward, up, around, back, and relax. Inhale while rolling your shoulders forward, up and around; exhale while pushing them back. Do this every 10 minutes. This might sound unusually frequent, but it will keep your upper body supple and relaxed, and you will feel rested from its effect by day's end.

BACKACHE

CRT users are plagued by backache. Four major causes are:

- **poor posture**
- **long, uninterrupted work periods**
- **improper chairs**
- **stress**

You can ease or even get rid of your backache by following the suggested solutions to each problem. They almost always stop backache, and do so immediately. Thus, if you actively cover this section and do not find relief, ask your doctor or chiropractor to check out what ails you.

✔ POSTURE

Poor posture puts unneeded stress on your spine. Back muscles then work overtime in all the wrong ways to compensate for your incorrect sitting and standing positions. You begin to tire, then to get sore, then to hurt. Good posture, conversely, puts the least amount of stress on your spine. It is not, however, achieved without effort. You must consciously exercise good posture until it becomes second nature.

Although good workstation design would, in itself, promote good posture, the reality is that we are several years from this advanced design. This means you must remind yourself often — until it becomes second nature — of the need to sit up straight and walk straight.

When you sit, stand, or walk with good posture, you will feel discernibly different than when your shoulders are slumped.

Initially, your muscles may object to the change. You may not have used them for sitting straight since you were a child. However, after a few days, those muscles, aching to be used, will provide you added energy throughout the day. (For further discussion on posture, see "Optimizing Physical Health and Comfort: Posture.")

✔ WORK PERIODS

CRT work often calls for people to remain at terminals for long periods of time, but your body was made to move. Long work periods without a break can lead to backache and other problems. Stillness prevents proper blood circulation and can cause a problem known as "blood pooling." It also lowers blood pressure, and lower blood pressure can make you drowsy. Most of all, long periods between breaks are tiring, both physically and mentally. Tired workers make more mistakes.

The well-regarded Professor Jorgen Winkel of Sweden's Karolinska Institute has conducted numerous studies on what happens when you sit too long at your work. He writes and speaks repeatedly of problems brought on by "lack of physical variation." His works conclude that prolonged sitting and prolonged standing cause leg and foot swelling, both of which suggest an increase of cardiovascular strain.

Mr. Winkel recommends moving your legs about while seated at your desk.

- **Push up from your toes while seated, until you feel your calf muscles stretching. Move your knees first together and then apart.**
- **Pick your legs up from the knee, freeing your feet from the floor, and twist your feet and ankles.**

You will find that these actions also move your spine and

provide some exercise for your stomach muscles.

It might surprise you that productivity among CRT users *increases* with short, frequent breaks. After you establish the pattern of taking breaks, it won't surprise you at all. You feel better immediately; consequently, performance improves immediately.

So take more breaks. They needn't be long. Just a minute or two on the half-hour is adequate. Then, take a two- or three-minute break on the hour.

> *As early as 1981, the National Institute for Occupational Safety and Health, whose purpose is to protect the health of working Americans, recommended more frequent breaks for CRT users than for non-CRT-using clerical workers, particularly for people doing repetitive tasks at a monitor.*

Unfortunately, you may not be able to follow NIOSH's recommendation at this time. Because discomfort and other problems associated with CRT work are not well known, a number of managers do not yet realize the seriousness of the problems.

How can you possibly hurt when you are sitting absolutely still? No part of you is being wrenched; you aren't working with a pickax and shovel. Moreover, the lighting probably seems pleasant, and the room temperature is comfortable. How, then, can you possibly be tired or uncomfortable?

This is a reasonable reaction from one who doesn't know that long, uninterrupted periods of sitting are the major cause of backache.

You realize there are problems in CRT use. Alert your employer to savings resulting from increased morale, decreased absenteeism, and increased productivity. Results of studies and major articles are published with some frequency in newspapers and magazines. Copy each one you encounter and place it in the boss's "in" box. A list of publications reporting on computer workstation issues is included at the end of this book.

Remember, all of us are ultimately responsible for our quality of life. If your boss doesn't know something that he needs to know, share with him what you know. You can hardly be surprised that he is unaware if no one is informing him.

This has been my biggest problem in this work. It is true that management on the whole *is* uninformed about CRT-user problems. But it is equally true that the CRT user isn't bringing the problems to management's attention.

To complicate matters further, when a compassionate boss asks if problems exist, the CRT user often does not give a forthright answer for fear of being seen as a complainer or troublemaker. Nevertheless, the employee is angry at the boss: "How could he possibly not know?"

The CRT user often doesn't respond well to questioning. Sadly, the fear of losing employment, or being thought of as a complainer, results in maintaining an uncomfortable workplace.

✔CHOOSING THE PROPER CHAIR

CRTs require special setups and arrangements to maintain worker comfort and efficiency. When a keyboard, monitor, and hard copy can be adjusted easily, the user is much less bothered by physical problems.

To complete correct workstation arrangement, you need a proper chair, one which supports the back and allows the feet to touch the floor. Most new chair models have several adjustable features, but these are not altogether necessary. In mid-1988, I spoke with the representative of a major American manufacturer of office furniture. I was told the manufacturer had found that users don't trouble with all the bells, horns and whistles of these

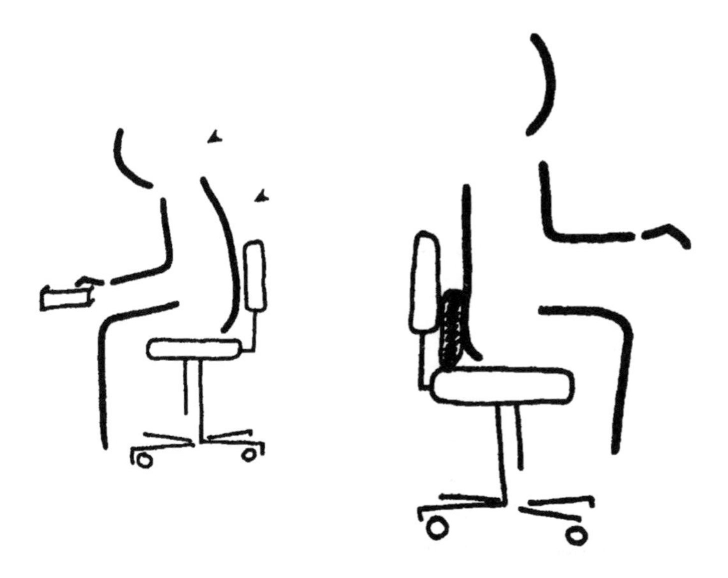

advanced designs, and the manufacturer would soon stop offering so many adjustable features.

The idea is to get a chair that basically is a good fit and feels comfortable. For this purpose I've included a form at the end of this section to help you decide whether a chair is right for you. Take the form with you when you shop for a chair.

If you buy a chair with many features, be sure these include:

- **a back rest that is adjustable in height;**
- **back rest *angle* adjustability;**
- **arms that are adjustable in height and are removable (the best are adjustable in width also);**
- **a seat that is adjustable in height (the best have a lever which adjusts height with fingertip control).**

If you feel you need, but don't have, a chair with these preferred qualities, you can still act to decrease or prevent backache.

Making Do with the Chair You Have

If the seat of your chair is too deep, place a cushion behind your back. Start with a one-inch-thick cushion. If the seat is too low and not adjustable, sit on a cushion to raise your body. Be sure the chair doesn't tilt your body forward or backward. The backrest should support you but not pitch you forward or backward into poor posture.

✔ STRESS

Stress causes a host of problems. Oddly, stress is a natural part of you. In fact, it is essential to survival. Excess stress, however, can be damaging. Remember your deep breathing exercises — a great stress reliever. The other great reliever of stress is leaving your workstation, if only for 60 seconds.

If you can't get away from your desk regularly, perform this simple exercise:

- **rock your spine left and right**
- **lean back**
- **hunch shoulders forward**
- **roll your shoulders and spine backwards**

ARMS, HANDS, AND WRISTS

Wearing down the structure of the arm and hand is of more concern to the computer operator than muscle fatigue. The tendons of the muscles which control the hands and fingers are of particular concern. Damage, though not frequently reported, can be very painful when it occurs and can require lengthy and expensive medical treatment.

Rhythmic contraction of muscles compresses blood vessels, causing waste products in the blood to be pumped out of the

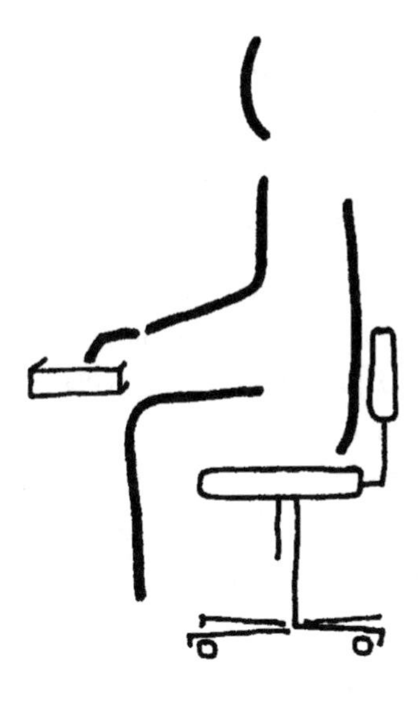

If your keyboard is too low, it will cause upper arm tension.

muscles. Every muscle contraction is followed by muscle relaxation, during which time nourishment flows to the muscles. *During static work, muscle activity is reduced, waste products are not thrown off, and circulation is slowed.*

Maintaining fixed postures, as called for in CRT work, means that muscles are generally in a constant state of contraction. The stationary nature of computer work does not mean that the muscles are not working.

In fact, precisely because muscles *are* working, two related biological problems can arise during static CRT work: Waste products can fail to be adequately removed and adequate nourishment can fail to reach the muscles.

✔ PREVENTING PROBLEMS

- **Set up your work area to avoid awkward elbow and wrist positions and movements.**

- **Take frequent rest breaks.**
- **Let your fingers do the keyboard work. Do not exert effort from your wrists.**
- **Strenthen your hands, wrists, and fingers through exercise by repeatedly squeezing a red rubber ball.**

Red rubber balls, the sort you may have played jacks with when you were a youngster, are very good for strengthening your hands, wrist and fingers. Simply hold one of the balls in each hand, squeezing one, then the other.

This is an exercise you can do at home, when you are sitting watching TV, or just in conversation with someone. Start with five minutes a day, and build up to 10 minutes.

If your keyboard is too high, it can invert the wrist action, thereby hitting the median nerve and causing pain.

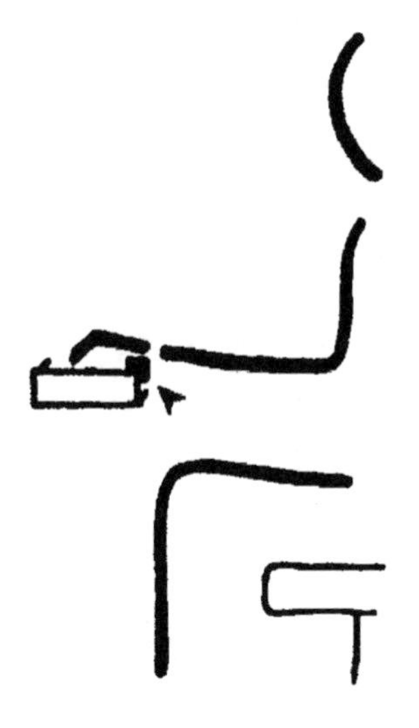

Wrist rests provide a cushion between the wrist and the work surface.

✔ RELIEVING FATIGUE WITH EXERCISE

The upper arm muscles move your lower arms and hands across the keyboard. Use the few seconds of response time during which your computer completes your word-processing or other commands to relieve tightness and fatigue in your arms, elbows, and wrists:

FOR ARMS

- **Stretch the upper and lower arm to work out that tightness at the inside of the elbow.**
- **Hold your arms out to your sides and down a bit, then push them back behind you while pushing your chest forward.**
- **Take a quick deep breath.**
- **Hold your arms straight out to your sides and move your hands in circular motions, first twisting the hands forward, then backward.**

- **Drop your arms to your sides and just shake them.**
- **Make a loose fist. Flex your inside lower arm muscles by gently bending your fist inward. Be gentle. Swift, severe movements can hurt your wrists.**

FOR ELBOWS

- **Drop your arms to your sides. Alternately rotate your hands so that your palms face inside and back, then outside and open. Repeat this five times.**

- **Hold your arms straight out, level with your shoulders. Pull your hands toward your head, as in "making a muscle." Pull tight. Relax. Put your arms straight out again, this time with your hands facing the floor. Now pull your hands in toward your chest.**

When talking on the telephone, do not rest the weight of your body on your elbows.

FOR WRISTS

- **Use only the minimum force necessary to depress the computer keys. Again, the force should come from the fingers, not from the hands and wrists.**
- **Build up strength in your fingers by exercising them with rubber balls, as mentioned above.**
- **Make a gentle fist. Pull your hands in, and push out. This will pull across the top of the wrists. Be very gentle. Rotate your fists in a small circular motion.**

Exercise the full length of your arms, from shoulder to fingertip, at every opportunity, ever watchful of not straining your wrists.

Do not rest your chin on your hand for long periods.

✔ REPETITIVE STRAIN INJURY

Repetitive Strain Injury (RSI) is clearly the major occupational hazard of the 1990s. RSI generally results when a combination of elements is present. Heretofore, repetitive motion has been identified as the cause of this condition.

In the present edition of this book, we introduce information we have been studying for several years, what we believe are the four common elements in RSI, three having been overlooked until this printing.

In addition to making the same movement over and over, what we believe are critical and additional elements common to RSI among computer users are:

improper use of the neck
poorly designed keyboards; and
previous cervical spine injury.

Because the wrist is the source of excruciating pain experienced by those with RSI, the keyboard has long been singled out as the cause of RSI. However, here, we propose that monitor placement and reference material stand placement, not the keyboard, are major contributors to causing RSI. When incorrectly positioned (too low, or too far to one side), the cervical spine (that's what your neck is wrapped around) is also incorrectly positioned. By definition, most computer workers sit all day, looking down at their monitors. When neck muscles must hold up a very heavy head all day, they ultimately clamp down and spasm atop nerves running throughout the back, down the arm, and up into the hand. Ouch.

Then there is the problem of keyboards. While keyboards do not, in my opinion, cause Carpal Tunnel Syndrome (CTS), all keyboards, I like to point out, are not created equal. In the Resources section, I note a particular keyboard, the Maltron, which we are finding greatly relieves, even eliminates, in some cases, RSI.

We believe the complete redesign of the keyboard is responsible for the favorable reviews it is receiving from computer users.

As noted in detail in the Resources section, the keyboard is not only changed in its basic design (layout and lettering) but it employs concave (scooped) keys so that shorter fingers travel no further than longer fingers. We believe this revolutionary design takes pressure off neck and shoulder muscles, thereby bringing enormous relief to RSI and non-RSI workers alike.

The most significant of our findings relates to previous injury to the cervical spine. In Appendix I, we describe the results of a "Retrospective" — not a study, as there were no controls employed — involving thirteen RSI patients of the Dickson Chiropractic Clinic in Winston-Salem, North Carolina.

It is interesting to note that nine of thirteen RSI patients had suffered previous cervical injury, a truly remarkable 77%.

My experience suggests that this is not coincidental. Physical therapists and occupational therapists have told me for years that at least half their patients have experienced previous cervical trauma. The emphasis is always on the "at least."

Preliminary results we've obtained employing new — together or as stand-alone — techniques (repositioning workstation element, use of the Maltron keyboard, and chiropractic adjustment, among other techniques) lead us to believe RSI will soon be treated along the lines of the protocol developed by Dr. Dickson at CDSI.

It is imperative to point out that there are other causes of RSI, including congential deformation and tumor growth. These of course will call for treatment by medical doctors and, probably, surgery. In the meantime, as the preponderance of incidence lies with the former identifications, we believe our findings will prove revolutionary in the field of identifying and treating RSI, and we hope they serve you well.

✔ WHAT IS CARPAL TUNNEL SYNDROME?

CTS, like other repetitive strain injuries, is a cumulative condition, often taking years to develop. Because of this, and because its symptoms are often more severe at night, CTS is not always associated with office work. Some sufferers experience the injury as arriving suddenly and unexpectedly, causing violent pain and leaving them unable to use their hands and lower arms. For others, the pain is less severe.

FREQUENCY OF CTS

A few short years ago, Carpal Tunnel Syndrome acounted for a modest two percent of all workplace illness, according to the Occupational Safety and Health Administration (OSHA). Today, it accounts for over half of all workplace illness. Almost 6 million people now suffer from Repetitive Strain Injury, most of which involves Carpal Tunnel Syndrome, according to *CDT News.* Nationally, CTS annually affects some 230,000 workers, costing each victim about $3,500 in benefits and rehabilitation, for a total cost of about $800 million according to a *Time* Magazine story published in October 1992.

NIOSH estimates that more than half of all U.S. workers are in jobs with the potential for repetitive strain disorder, including nearly half the work force, or some 60 million workers, who use computers.

Some 100,000 cases were deemed appropriate for surgery in 1992 at a cost of about $24,000 per worker.

SERIOUSNESS OF CTS

A 25-fold increase in five years is grim news. And the disorder is likely still on the rise, as CTS is a cumulative condition which often takes years to develop.

- **CTS is generally excrutiatingly painful;**
- **It can be debilitating;**
- **Workers' Compensation costs average $24,000;**
- **Surgery is the conventional treatment;**
- **Surgery plus recovery generally costs almost $30,000;**
- **Surgery is not only painful, but often not successful.**

WHAT CAUSES CTS?

Carpal Tunnel Syndrome results from the pinching of the median nerve which runs the length of the arm and wrist and into the hand. This nerve has its "home" in the cervical part of the spine, in what is called the C-7, C-8 nerve root area. The seventh cervical, just to locate it for you, is the very prominent vertebra protruding about three inches below the base of the skull.

Among those reporting discomfort or pain, I find that most, when asked, report that they have also experienced severe neckache and discomfort at this part of the spine. Improper use of neck muscles can exert pressure on the originating point of the nerve associated with Carpal Tunnel Syndrome. Neck muscles, exhausted by holding up the head under conditions of excessive strain, finally spasm. They grip the C-7 area like a vise, causing severe pain to shoot down the arm and through the hand where the median nerve branches terminate.

Other signs include numbness of the hand, inability to maintain a hand grip, tingling (especially at night), swelling on the palm side of the wrist, and a "pins and needles" sensation in the arms and hands; finally, excruciating pain.

While all keyboards are not created equal, their role in CTS is mostly one of exacerbating, not causing, the condition. Also exacerbating the condition is lack of frequent work breaks.

IS CTS AVOIDABLE?

Carpal Tunnel Syndrome is avoidable. Avoidance calls for proper workstation setup. Micro-breaks of two to three minutes on the half hour, coupled with in-place exercise, also prevent stress from setting in. However, once CTS is contracted, it may take more than proper work habits to reverse it.

WORKSTATION

This is the formula for setting up a workstation that will help you avoid CTS:

- **Place your monitor at approximately eye level so that your head can balance atop the natural pivot of the neck. Your head weighs about as much as a bowling ball. Supporting it for long periods at an awkward angle can easily overstress the neck muscles.**
- **Place your reference material stand at eye level, close to your monitor. This will "let your eyes do the walking."**
- **Position your keyboard so that your upper arms hang naturally at your sides and your forearms rest parallel to the floor**

BREAKS

For those spending long hours and days at a monitor, brief but frequent work breaks have such a positive effect on the worker and on output that I have come to call them "productivity breaks." Investment in computers and workstations is so high that employees are kept at their stations, without respite, in an effort to maximize output and, therefore, overall return. Alas, stress and other health problems clearly identified with this work pattern have the opposite effect on "the bottom line."

Once stress has locked into the neck and shoulder area, it is very difficult to eliminate. Workers can prevent stress buidup by taking micro-breaks of two to three minutes on the half hour, during which time they can do head, neck, and shoulder rolls coupled with deep breathing. (One should note that allocating time for productivity breaks — two to three minutes per half hour, or five to seven minutes per hour — amounts to allocating less time than the 15 mintues per two hours recommended by others.)

EXERCISE

Exercise is useful. It strengthens muscles. Your physical therapist and your chiropractor are generally at the ready with specific exercises for specific parts of the body. To help prevent CTS, ask for upper body exercises.

Also take time to do simple arm and wrist exercises, being careful not to strain the delicate wrist areas. Whatever exercise you do, remember that it should never cause pain or discomfort

VITAMINS

The most intriguing information I've encountered comes from Marion Ellis, M.D., Mt. Pleasant, Texas, who has conducted considerable research into vitamin B6.

A native of the cotton-growing area of East Texas, Dr. Ellis observed that prior to the commonplace bleaching of the wheat flour used to make bread, cotton workers might pick 300-400 pounds of cotton daily without complaining of wrist problems. Early cotton pickers were likely to have consumed more vitamin B6 than do their later counterparts because bleaching wheat robs it of nutrients — including vitamin B6. Only a few of wheat's 20-odd nutrient components are returned to it during modern processing.

Dr. Ellis suggests a relationship between wrist problems and vitamin B6. He recommends supplementing a healthy diet with 100 mg. of vitamin B6 daily. Because the B vitamins are water soluble, they are thrown off as water leaves the body; to maintain a steady level of the vitamin, Dr. Ellis recommends taking 50 mg. in the morning and 50 mg. at night. Ninety percent of Dr. Ellis's patients who suffered from wrist problems responded to B6 treatment within twelve weeks.

Dr. Tom Dickson, chiropractor and nutritionist practicing in Winston-Salem, North Carolina, explains that because the B vitamins are never found isolated in nature, many nutritionists belive that they work best when taken in a complete B-complex tablet such as a B-50, so called because it contains 50 mg. of each of the 16 available B vitamins. Dr. Dickson points out that B6, used in conjunction with a B-50, can produce the best results in the control of edematous buildup — fluid retention — that can congest the carpal tunnel and subsequently reduce axial nerve flow. The B vitamins have been found to be helpful in reducing edema surrounding the various "tunnels" of the body. Reducing localized fluid buildup helps to decongest the carpal tunnel.

CHIROPRACTIC

When a person in pain visits a good chiropractor, misaligned vertebrae are put right, a weight lifting and strengthening exercise program is prescribed, and the patient is told why he must place his monitor and reference material stand at approximately eye level. Soon enough the patient is out of pain and out of danger.

Dr. Dickson finds that those returning with a flare-up of the original discomfort and pain usually have failed to follow through with the exercise program outlined, and have failed to reconfigure their workstations. Because a number of the failed surgery cases have previous cervical trauma (whiplash), the incidence of recurrence of symptoms in the cervical spine and arm nerve complex is higher among these trauma victims.

Postural strain due to incorrect monitor use will reproduce carpal and arm symptoms. Due to damage to the nerve itself, close monitoring of neck posture will further the correction process. In conclusion, Dr. Dickson feels that the high-risk group of VDT workers with previous cervical trauma must pay especially close attention to optimal workstation setup.

WRISTWRAPS

Some authorities believe that workers should not use wristwraps while working at the keyboard, but only before and after work. They believe that the tensions of working against the restriction of the wraps, however slight, applies further pressure to the injured area. However, some workers find it comfortable to wear wraps while working. Judge for yourself.

Wristwraps can be made from handkerchiefs, or of Ace bandages. Wrap *lightly*. The goal is to *slightly* restrict movement while not constricting blood flow.

CAN SURGERY BE AVOIDED?

Considering or scheduled for surgery? Chiropractors are experts in reducing nerve pressure in the cervical spine. Ask your chiropractor to check the C-5, C-6, C-7, and T-1 vertebrae of your upper spine. Numerous alternative therapies exist and should be explored: Massage therapy, physical therapy, and acupunture are but a few.

Different bodies respond differently to various treatments. On reflection, however, it seems the most successful outcome is reached by following the three-pronged approach which includes chiropractic adjustment of the cervical spine, setting one's monitor and reference material stand at eye level, and using vitamin B6 coupled with a B-complex such as B-50.

Photocopy the following checklist and affix it to your monitor or to a surface nearby. It will remind you of what you can be doing to avoid CTS.

• Monitor at eye level to avoid overtaxing the neck?

• Reference materials stand at eye level?

• Elbows at 90-degree angles and arms straight from elbow to fingertip to minimize flexing of wrists?

• Had your B vitamins?

• Stop, roll your head in a circular motion to relax the neck muscles; push your shoulders up and back to stretch them.

• How long since you took a quick break? Walk away from your desk, breathe deeply for a minute or two, stretch.

✓ CARING FOR THE WRISTS

Looking at the back of your hand, examine the protruding wrist bone. Turn the palm of your hands in toward you, and you find the flipside of the pisiform bone at the inside of the wrist.

It is easy to hit this bone on the desktop when keying in data. Every time you rest your hands you chance striking this bone. Bruising it and the surrounding flesh can be uncomfortable, even painful. Protect the pisiform bone by doing these things:

• Place the full width of the hand, or the fleshy, outer part of the hand, on the desktop when you pause.

• Make wrist rests to protect the pisiform bones. Use pieces of sponge or foam rubber ¼- to ½-inch thick. Affix them to your desk where your wrists lie. Use adhesive that won't leave marks if the wrist rests are removed.

• Make your own wrist wraps using handkerchiefs or Ace bandages. Wrap *lightly*. The purpose is to alert you to excess movement. Be careful not to constrict blood flow.

Another approach to the relief of wrist stress is use of keyboards designed with the wrist action in mind. I found one such keyboard on a recent trip to London. It is called the Maltron, and is discussed fully in the Resources section of this book.

LEGS AND FEET

CRT users can blame ill-fitting chairs for most leg and foot discomfort. Although a new chair can be a wonderful thing, it isn't the total solution to leg and foot discomfort. Leaving your workstation for walks is always a good idea, no matter what kind of chair you have. Using the smallest of cushions — be sure it is the smallest — and a footstool can also improve comfort.

But even the best seating arrangement cannot prevent discomfort. You *must sit properly.* Always use good posture. Simply *never* sit with your legs crossed and pulled up into the chair seat. This cuts off circulation of blood from your upper leg to your lower leg. Think about that.

If you sit with good posture and still feel numbness in your legs, your chair probably needs to be adjusted because it is cutting off blood flow. The necessary adjustment required depends on whether the numbness is in the upper leg, lower leg, or along the entire leg.

✔ UPPER LEG

Numbness in the upper leg generally occurs when the chair seat is higher than your lower leg is long. Because your feet aren't planted firmly on the floor, the weight of your legs presses the undersides of your upper legs, cutting off blood to your lower leg.

- **If your upper legs become numb, you probably need to lower the seat of your chair.**

Many CRT operators don't know how to adjust their chairs. If you don't know how, ask someone to help you. Don't feel silly or shy; remember most people enjoy helping others.

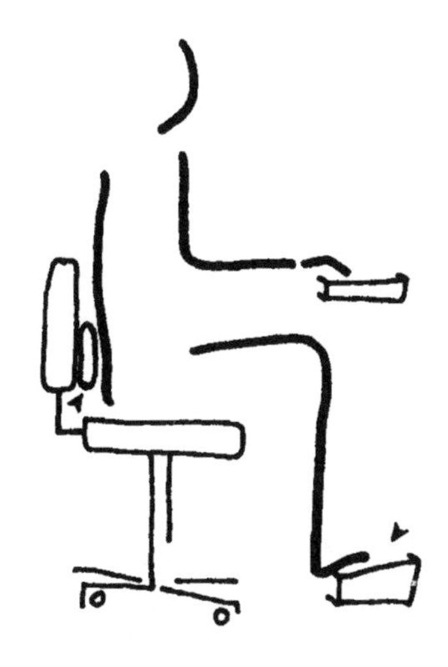

- **If your seat is already as low as it will go, try placing a low footstool under your feet. Putting your feet on it will raise your upper leg (at the knee) off the edge of the chair seat. This should help improve circulation.**

Make the footstool of anything. A block of wood, probably masquerading at the lumberyard as scrap, will serve well. Even a cardboard box will do. You can get one at the grocery store where the empty cartons are thrown.

Lumber height or box height will depend on how much you need to add to the bottom half of your legs. A block of wood might be two or three inches high. Suitable cardboard boxes might include those for small tomato-paste cans (about three inches high) or regular tomato-soup cans (about five inches high).

Be careful not to raise your feet so high that your knees scrape the underside of your desk.

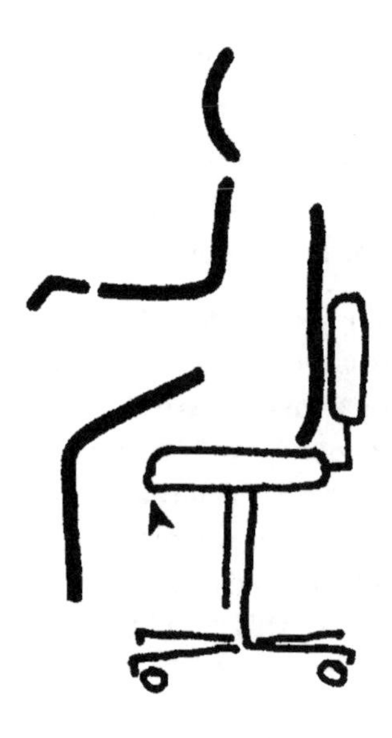

If the chair is too high, it prevents feet from being planted firmly on the floor, thus impairing circulation.

✔ LOWER LEG

Numbness in the lower leg can occur when the length of the chair seat is greater than the distance from the back of your buttocks to the back of your bent knees.

The Three-Finger Test

> *If three fingers slip comfortably back and forth between the leading edge of the chair seat and the back of your leg, the space is adequate for proper circulation.*

If your can't slip two or three fingers into this space, and lower leg numbness is a problem, try using a footstool. Push the stool forward a bit so your legs won't have constant contact with the front of the chair. A small cushion at your back also might help. If you feel forced to use a large cushion, you probably need a different chair.

Numbness along the entire leg and foot may also require you to change chairs. It means the seat is both too high and too deep for your body. A footstool might help, if it is pushed forward so your legs don't contact the front edge of the chair seat, but you probably need a different chair.

The 30/60 Rule

Every 30 minutes, get up and leave your workstation for 60 seconds. Walk around. If you have time, go to the restroom for a stretch. Try the stretching techniques suggested below.

✔STRETCHES FOR LEG RELIEF

You can do a great deal to relieve tension and discomfort in your legs by doing a few simple stretches. Try these stretches.

INSIDE THIGH

- **Stand with your feet about a yard apart. Bend your right knee by moving your weight onto your right foot. Inhale as you bend the knee. Hold the position. Straighten the knee. Exhale as you straighten. Repeat with the left leg.**

BACK OF THE LEG

- **Put your feet together. Inhale deeply. Exhale slowly on the way down to touch your toes. Inhale on the way up. And put your feet apart.**
- **Turn your right foot out. This will shift your weight to your left leg. Bend the left knee as far as you can. Inhale as you bend. Hold the position. Straighten, exhaling as you do. Turn the right foot back to the front. Repeat with the right leg.**

FRONT OF THE LEG

• Put your right foot two or three feet in front of your left foot. Moving your weight onto your right foot, bend the right knee. Inhale slowly as you bend slowly. Exhale, and straighten. Repeat with the left leg.

Initially, you may need to touch a wall with one hand in order to maintain your balance. Otherwise just use your arms for balance, holding them up and away from your sides, bent forward at the elbow. You should be able to do the above six bends in less than one minute. Combining deep breathing with leg bends lowers blood pressure and improves full body circulation.

Numerous companies still are not comfortable with short but frequent breaks for computer operators. If you cannot get away from your desk often, rely on constant deep breathing for relaxation and improving your circulation.

In closing this section, I should point out that the fortunate among you with open-minded bosses might refer them to the results of paid exercise breaks, as researched by David A. Thompson, Ph.D., at Stanford University. (There's more on this in the Stress section of this book.)

OPTIMIZING PHYSICAL HEALTH AND COMFORT: POSTURE

Before the Industrial Revolution, people worked in a cyclical pattern. Farmers labored to plant in the spring, harvested with vigor in the fall, then rested through winter before repeating the cycle — strenuous work followed by periods of prolonged rest.

The Industrial Revolution put an end to all that. Workers were forced into repetitive, nonstop days that changed only for a few vacation days per year. Our new work patterns created tissue fatigue and chronic degenerative conditions.

Constant sitting, however, particularly as experienced by the full-time computer user, brought on new physical demands. The low back curve was reduced as the main trunk muscles fought to hold the body erect. Since sitting work requires inclining slightly forward, the neck was forced to hold the head from falling too far forward. This was compounded by the outstretched arms that created shoulder muscle fatigue. And this resulted in the chronic muscle fatigue pattern of the lower back, upper back and neck as well as degenerative disc disease in the low back and neck.

Computer operators are the epitome of chronic postural maladaption. They are subject to extreme compensatory muscle and degenerative changes resulting from chronic inactivity under postural and gravitational stress.

Posture is a function of workstation design and good workstation design will evoke good posture. A perfect chair and workstation, however, will not prevent backache generally attributed to poor posture. You must practice good posture, vary physical position frequently, and leave your workstation regularly, if briefly.

Whether sitting or standing, good posture means

- **The head is held high,**
- **The chin is held slightly up,**
- **The shoulders are held up and back,**
- **The spine is erect from the top of the neck to the buttocks,**
- **The lower back is relaxed and brought forward into a comfortable slump and,**
- **The abdomen is relaxed.**

The first three points are associated with the universally recommended 90-degree angle seated posture, whereby a 90-degree angle is formed at major joints. The other three points are associated with Feldenkrais and other teaching methods which attempt to minimize discomfort associated with sitting for long periods of time.

It is critical to sitting comfort, whether sitting erect or leaning slightly back in your chair or standing, that all these points be covered.

To account for people who are only comfortable in a backward leaning posture, it should be noted that E. Grandjean and his colleagues in their 1983 study found that given a fully adjustable chair, many subjects preferred a trunk inclination of 100-110 degrees, which position reduces intervertebral back pressure. (Most manufacturers now offer back angle adjustability as a feature of their chairs. Though these chairs can be very comfortable and allow nicely for leaning back to stretch, they do not account for the increased angle change caused at the elbow if one leans back to work in this position. Note that the greater open angle at the elbow causes arm muscles to work harder than they must work when in the generally recommended 90-degree or less angle.)

Good posture puts the least amount of stress on your spine, calling on your neck and back muscles to do minimal work. Good posture isn't difficult but it is achieved only through diligence. You must work consciously to evoke good posture. Eventually it will become second nature, and doing it wrong will feel wrong, will feel unnatural. You'll be working at your desk, concentrating on something, and suddenly . . . oops, there are those rounded shoulders. You're slumping. Take a deep breath, relax, sit up straight, push your shoulders back and your back into a comfortable slump.

Frequent breaks enhance posture. As early as 1981, the National Institute for Occupational Safety and Health, whose purpose it is to protect the health of the American worker, recommended more frequent breaks for CRT users than for non-CRT-using clerical workers, particularly for those doing repetitive tasks at a monitor.

Practice deep breathing during sitting and all other times. Deep breathing maximizes relaxation, minimizing blood pressure and needless pressures inflicted on the body.

If your chair allows, lean back in it every 15 or so minutes for a stretch. This will relieve spinal pressure that builds up over time.

Loose clothing enhances comfort.

A pillow at the small of the back can be comfortable, but be sure it is a small pillow.

When standing long periods, try to keep one foot a few inches higher than the other, and alternating feet.

Optimum posture is one solution to the problems brought on by constant sitting demands.

Starting on the following page is my Chair Evaluation Form© for helping select a chair that, in meeting your physical requirements, abets optimum work posture. I urge you to take a copy of it on chair shopping trips and to share it with everyone at your company who helps decide what furniture will be used.

CHAIR EVALUATION FORM ©

	Agree	Disagree	Not Applicable
BACK REST:			
At no point do I feel the backrest cutting into my back.	❑	❑	❑
The shape of the backrest seems to fit the shape of my back fairly well.	❑	❑	❑
The chair supports me well when I lean back: that is, it prevents my leaning unnaturally & uncomfortably far.	❑	❑	❑
I can lean back in the chair about as far as I like.	❑	❑	❑
SEAT:			
I do not sink into the seat such that it is difficult to move about: that is, the seat feels reasonably firm.	❑	❑	❑
The seat adjusts to the correct height: that is, the top side of the front rim leaves my thigh feeling free and without pressure from the below the thigh.	❑	❑	❑
The seat offers the correct length: that is, the length from my buttocks to the back of my knees is about right. The calves of my lower leg feel free of the seat's edge.	❑	❑	❑

ARMRESTS:	Agree	Disagree	Not Applicable
The armrests are not too far apart: that is, they support my arms when at rest.	❑	❑	❑
The armrests do not crowd me: that is, my arms feel a comfortable distance from the sides of my body.	❑	❑	❑
The armrests do not interfere with the movements of my arms.	❑	❑	❑
As I work, the armrests do not bump the desk.	❑	❑	❑
As I work, my elbows do not bump the backrest of the chair.	❑	❑	❑
It does not require too much effort or pressure to operate the chair controls.	❑	❑	❑
I do not become confused using the controls, adjusting one when I meant to adjust the other.	❑	❑	❑
All the adjustment mechanisms work fairly smoothly, allowing me to change the various positions of the chair in small increments.	❑	❑	❑
I can easily reach the controls from a sitting position.	❑	❑	❑
OVERALL:			
The chair moves about easily.	❑	❑	❑
The chair doesn't roll away uncontrolled.	❑	❑	❑
Overall, the chair is quite comfortable. I feel rested at the end of a day's use.	❑	❑	❑
Desk accommodates chair height	❑	❑	❑

VISUAL

THE WORKSTATION AND VISUAL PROBLEMS

Terminals started to flood the market only ten years ago. In this short time, about 75 million have been placed in operation, the bulk of them in the workplace. In 1989 alone, 10 million new monitors reached the marketplace.

There is concern that CRT use causes eye damage and eye deterioration. However, it still hasn't been determined whether CRTs are harmful to vision and, if so, to what extent. Numerous studies are underway, and others — an embarrassingly small handful — are complete but inconclusive. It probably will be years before definitive study is concluded, because it must report results of years of cumulative effect on vision.

What is certain is that complaints of eye trouble are legion among CRT users. We know pain and discomfort are the body's ways of warning against abuse — or worse, impending breakdown — of one or more of its systems. An enlightening study conducted by Dr. Jim Sheedy of the University of California Eye Clinic in Berkeley. Dr. Sheedy found that "[CRT] users in their twenties and thirties are suffering vision problems that usually develop after age 40."[1] CRT operators suffering from vision problems associated with poor workstation setup may need glasses sooner than usual, and may change into new prescriptions with disturbing frequency.

If you bought this book because you are thinking of taking a job working at a monitor, call your eye doctor now for an

1. As reported by Carol Matlack in the December 3, 1988 issue of National Journal, p. 3070.

appointment. Working at a monitor means, first and foremost, you must monitor the health of your eyes. It's perplexing, but companies still do not test potential employees to determine whether their eyes are suited to CRT work. Employers try to determine if we are qualified as typists, engineers, accountants, carpenters, painters, astronauts, truck drivers, etc. Yet we still do not test vision skills of employees whose job description might include reading accurately and without difficulty, with or without glasses.

Good vision skills are critical to high productivity. Studies have shown that good vision skills mean greater correct reading rate and higher morale.

How do we attain good visual health? Rate as a highly accurate CRT-using employee? Minimize the need for eyeglass change? Let's look at a plan that abets optimum visual health.

The CRT User's Guide to Good Visual Health

Your eyes were designed for long distance vision — for hunting and watching for the approaching enemy. They were not designed for reading, which occurs at arm's length, and they were especially not designed for working at a computer terminal for most of an eight-hour day with little, if any, relief.

Remember that the transition from hunter to farmer to factory has occurred over tens of thousands of years. The later move from factory to office has occurred within a scant hundred years. Nature dictates where we hold and how we handle tools, thus we place the typewriter in front of us, "at arm's length," because that's where we can reach it. However, arm's length isn't eye's length, as we shall see.

Because of the habitual reliance on arm's length, the first personal computers were multi-headed monsters grafted onto a single trunk. Monitor, keyboard and storage unit comprised the whole. No component part — monitor, keyboard, nor storage unit — could be individually adjusted, forcing fixed positions on the body and fixed focusing of the eyes such as had never before been known in the workplace. Eventually, both the monitor and the keyboard were separated from the central processing unit to allow for individual adjustment. Design work still is needed. But the monolith monster has been slain.

Although the CRT is now manufactured in three adjustable component parts, our work is still done at near vision. A constant battle is waged by the arm and hand against the eye. Tragically, the eye is the loser, and if it could talk instead of only seeing, this is what you'd probably hear:

ARM & HAND: *"Read this."*
EYE: *"I can't."*
ARM & HAND: *"Why not?"*
EYE: *"I just can't. I can't see it properly."*
ARM & HAND: *"What do you mean?"*
EYE: *"I can't focus. It's too close."*
ARM & HAND: *"Sorry. Can't help."*

What does this say about how we sit and where we place ourselves in relation to our monitors? A great deal.

In the majority of workstations that I have seen the monitor is placed 18 to 24 inches from the user. This is also what generally is recommended in most diagrams and technical journals.

> *If you use only one piece of information in this book, let it be this:* ***Sitting too close to your monitor violates nature's basic design of the eye's focusing mechanism.***

Violation of this first law of CRT use — as with any improper use of your eyes — almost always results in a host of problems: Eyestrain, eye fatigue, eyeball ache, blurred vision, burning eyes, watery eyes, and other discomforts.

Fortunately, there are solutions that are easy to implement; moreover, most of them are cost-free. In the following pages, I have presented solutions I've found effective for almost 100% of my CRT clients. If you follow all my suggestions you can prevent further problems.

I repeatedly recommend three solutions in particular for most eye problems, even though the problems are different.

First, I set the monitor three to four feet from my eyes, and strongly recommend you do the same. (I must say this is made feasible due to the type of anti-glare filter I use. Because this screen makes lettering crisp, the screen becomes readable at quite some distance. Without this filter, you may not be able to work at this distance. See the Resources section for more information.)

Second, I use, and strongly recommend, a particular anti-glare filter. Time and again I mention this screen because I have found that it solves nearly every CRT-user vision problem I have encountered. This is in no way an overstatement. It is important, however, to recognize that this filter may not be correct for *your* eyes. It is uncommon, but not unheard-of, that someone cannot use such a filter. The section on CRT-User Products will tell you what you need to know about this.

Third, I use, and strongly recommend, frequent eye rests and eye exercises. You must remember that the eye is controlled by numerous muscles and a very complex neurological system. Like all systems, the muscles of the eye can do only so much work; then they must rest.

If you intend to maintain the health of your eyes, you must recognize this fact. If your job requires a full day (four or five hours) at the monitor, you *must* spend four to five minutes per hour away from your monitor.

If you follow closely the subsequent guidelines for eliminating specific problems, an overwhelming majority of you can expect to have no problems whatever with your vision.

Finally, pick up the telephone right now and schedule an appointment with an eye doctor. See the Vision Evaluation Form©.

MAJOR ELEMENTS OF VISUAL PROBLEMS

Most computer users who spend four or more hours daily at a monitor report a variety of vision problems. Many report several problems. Eyes can burn or water. They can be dry; they can itch; they can be dry and itchy. Eyestrain and eye tiredness are frequently reported.

The major elements of CRT-user visual problems are:

- **nearness of eyes to the monitor;**
- **brightness of the monitor's image;**
- **length of time spent at the monitor;**
- **sensitivity of eyes to light;**
- **poor resolution of the monitor's lettering.**

Eliminating vision problems entails setting up your computer terminal correctly, adjusting brightness for your eyes' sensitivity, and taking eye breaks. (You'll find specific complaints, such as burning eyes or blurred vision, and solutions listed in the next segment. But first read this segment.)

NEARNESS OF EYES TO THE MONITOR

Try reading the monitor from a distance of six to eight feet. If you can't distinguish any of the lettering, move a foot or so closer, and try again. Stay at this distance for 30 seconds so your

eyes will adjust. Continue this pattern, moving closer to the monitor each time, holding each new position until your eyes adjust. When you establish what seems to be the best distance for you, try moving 6-12 inches closer. The most comfortable position is generally a bit closer than the position that allows readability only.

You can establish correct monitor position in reverse, of course. Set the monitor several feet from your eyes. Moving the screen back seems to soften screen brightness and usually makes focusing easier. Try the monitor at 30 inches. If this is comfortable, try 35 inches, then 40, etc.

It is distinctly easier for most people to read a monitor from afar — it's easier for their eyes to work at a distance. In addition, monitor images generally are perceived as crisper at greater than the standard 18 to 28 inches.

I have spoken at length with a researcher who has conducted at least one CRT vision study with a major American computer manufacturer. Emphasis was on the distance between the user and the monitor. Results indicated that the ability to distinguish lettering and other images on the monitor declines rapidly beyond a certain very close distance. This researcher pointed out that I was recommending that users sit too far from the monitors, and his tests substantiated his argument.

I must emphasize, however, that my favorable results in stopping eye problems were related to increased distance from the monitor *coupled with* use of the special anti-glare filter mentioned elsewhere. The filter enhances contrast by making the background very black (vs. just making the entire monitor darker, as do many anti-glare screens). In addition, the extremely fine fiber of the cloth makes the monitor lettering very crisp (vs. fuzzier, as do most other anti-glare screens). Together, these features allow the monitor to be set, quite comfortably, three or more feet from the user's eyes, allowing the eye muscles to work from a relaxed position.

I also suspect that research might one day suggest that reading images from emitted light (e.g., the monitor's images) is easier than it is from reflected light (e.g., printed matter). For instance, I suspect that a 10-foot high sign in green or yellow neon light set in the black of the night reading "CRT Operators are Wonderful People" can be read at a much greater distance than a similar 10-foot high sign in green or yellow ink on black paper billboard; or, for that matter, easier to read than the same billboard sign set in the dark of the night with megawatt spotlights shining on it.

One final comment on seating users at a distance from their monitors. An employee I worked with was most comfortable reading at a distance of seven feet from the monitor. Her boss insisted that she couldn't read from that distance. I said, "You mean *you* can't see from that distance." He agreed. When establishing the correct distance for you, consider only eye comfort and ease of focusing. These are inseparable concepts.

> *In positioning monitors, remember: Each part of your body is but a fraction of the uniqueness that is you. You — any CRT user — must set up the workstation based on what "feels right" for you. If my suggestions don't seem quite right, experiment with your workstation:* ***Make it right for you.***

BRIGHTNESS OF THE MONITOR'S IMAGE

The monitor should be the brightest object in the room, yet looking at the screen shouldn't hurt your eyes. Lowering room lighting enhances monitor contrast (the dark looks darker and the light looks lighter), making the images more distinct; it also allows the monitor's light to be lowered.

It is difficult, of course, to reduce overhead lighting in a room where different tasks are performed, in which case you might move your CRT to another part of the room, if possible.

Reduce the monitor brightness until you must strain slightly to read the lettering, until you sense that it is slightly difficult to read your monitor. After your pupil adjusts, increase the brightness just a bit — until you sense you are not straining to read your monitor.

> *Your aim is to set the intensity of the monitor's brightness where it "feels soft" on your eyes (an expression I've heard from the thousands of CRT users whose monitor brightness I have helped lower). "Oh, yes," they say, "I see. Now, that light feels soft on my eyes."*

LENGTH OF TIME SPENT AT THE MONITOR

The eye is designed to see comfortably and accurately at distances well beyond arm's length. Distance vision allows the muscles in each eye to be relaxed yet still control vision. As the object being viewed nears the eye — such as when reading, knitting, crafting leather work, etc. — the muscles controlling vision contract, or tighten. The closer the object to the eye, the tighter the eye muscles.

The contracting of these muscles causes no trouble when the tightening occurs for short periods of time — a few minutes, here and there. However, if contracted without pause, these muscles eventually cramp.

This cramping is what CRT-users refer to as "eye ache." Perhaps the expression "charley horse" rings a bell. *The Random House Dictionary* (1966) defines a "charley horse" as a "painful, involuntary contraction of an arm or leg muscle resulting from excessive muscular strain or a blow."

What happens in the case of CRT-user eye ache is that overworked eye muscles go into spasm — just as muscles do with other forms of "charley horse". The strain is distressing — the tendency is to rub one's eyes, which interrupts work. Eye ache can be uncomfortable, and often painful.

In many cases, CRTs simply cannot be pushed any farther from the eyes than they already are — the desk has no more depth, and the wall cannot be moved. If you can't lower the river, raise the bridge: Use your center drawer to hold your keyboard, effectively pushing you another foot away from your monitor.

Keep in mind that eye rests can be taken at your desk. Take every available opportunity to rest your eyes.

- **Glance away from your monitor at every possible chance.**

• Use computer response time for an opportunity to look away from your monitor.

• When pondering some issue, look away from your screen.

• Find a dark spot in the room. Concentrate on it. Darkness is restful to the eyes.

• If the room has no dark areas, create them. Cup your hands and place them over your eyes. Count slowly to five. The same amount of time allows you one deep, relaxing breath!

SENSITIVITY OF EYES TO LIGHT

Blue eyes and green eyes are more sensitive to light than brown eyes are. Brown eyes have added filtering which makes them generally less sensitive to brightness. Eyes which are hypersensitive to light will find numerous short breaks refreshing.

If your eyes are sensitive to brightness, be aware of surrounding light. Remember, the lower the room light, the softer you can make your monitor light. Sensitivity to light can cause frontal headache, which can indicate visual problems. This is covered in the next segment of this chapter.

Do everything you can to soften all sources of light. If you still experience headache, or if your eyes tire easily, be sure to have an eye examination.

It's especially irritating if your monitor "flickers" — throws off a blinking, unsteady image. Do not tolerate this inferior quality for long. Have maintenance workers determine whether too many monitors are connected to the same power supply, whether the starter switch is faulty, or whether the monitor is wearing out. If it is wearing out and cannot be repaired, have the monitor replaced.

Glare is especially troublesome to light-sensitive eyes. See the special segment on glare in this section.

POOR IMAGE RESOLUTION

A monitor whose lettering isn't crisp should be replaced. Monitors that produce "fuzzy" images cause at least two problems.

First, looking at such a monitor is tiring to the focus mechanism of the eyes. In my opinion, keeping these monitors is out of step with safeguarding vision.

Second, because the eyes cannot focus well, monitors with fuzzy lettering generally cause the user to make considerably more errors than usual. Auditing costs to correct resulting errors are usually much more than a new monitor.

Before replacing a faulty monitor, read the section entitled CRT-User Products. I mention the 20/20 anti-glare filter. I have been told by several academicians that a monitor's resolution cannot be corrected. This is technically correct. However, the particular anti-glare filter which I use not only gives the impression of correcting resolution, but CRT users who previously complained of eye ache are surprised that their eye ache ceases when they use this filter.

Also, note that a clean monitor gives the best picture possible. When dust settles on the monitor, display quality can deteriorate rapidly, and the fuzzy picture you see can be mistaken for poor resolution. Keep your monitor clean. (The best products are those which contain no ammonia. Water, for instance, works well. Rub the glass dry with newspaper or a paper towel.)

Now, let's look at solving some problems that arise when the elements discussed above are not taken into consideration.

Specific Visual Problems and Their Solutions

Optometrists estimate that at least 30% of office workers have vision problems which are undetected, uncorrected or undercorrected. Little wonder, then, that my statistics show complaint of eye tiredness (13%), eyestrain (61%), blurred vision (51%), and eyeball ache (27%) — many operators reporting three of the four conditions. If total responsibility for vision problems lie with the uncorrected problem alone, the maximum number of visual complaints would be the uncorrected 30% — clearly not the case. Vision problems — particularly the most uncomfortable of them — relate, it seems, to overuse and abuse of the ocular system.

By asking question after question; by trying to modify each question to fit the individual computer terminal user; by repositioning the monitor; by adjusting the monitor's light; through repeated telephone calls to the CRT user, I was able to help most CRT users rid themselves of most vision problems.

Don't be lulled into thinking that alleviating *your* specific visual problem means that your eye problems are over. Quite the contrary. Remember the odds are three in 10 that you fall into the 30% of CRT workers whose eyes need correcting prior to their going into office work. So even if vision problems have failed to surface to date, you are urged to have a proper eye examination before taking a job at a video display.

Because of the numerous and frequently expressed visual complaints of computer operators, I created a questionnaire to qualify and quantify the types and severity of complaints. I assumed that a pattern of problems and solutions eventually would emerge. In fact, the patterns emerged within the first week of using the questionnaire.

That study — dealing only with headache, neckache, eye-strain, and blurred vision — evolved into this book. Resolving vision problems gave me the most wonderful sense of satisfaction imaginable. Users said, "What did I ever do before you came along?" "How did I stand it for so long?" "Life is so different now. I actually come to work rested."

Of all problems encountered, eye problems exacted the greatest toll on most video display operators I worked with. Stopping their problems made them unusually grateful. This seems like the most appropriate place to tell you how grateful I would be if you would fill in the questionnaire located on page 30 and return it to me. It will take only a few minutes of your time. By providing detailed information which I can add to my log of information you will be helping others.

EYE PROBLEMS

Logging computer users' vision complaints and studying and analyzing their problems resulted in the following solutions. These solutions, coupled with use of the anti-glare filter that I tout repeatedly, minimize or eliminate most eye discomfort.

✔ EYE TIREDNESS, EYE FATIGUE

Eye tiredness seems to be the video display operator's initial visual complaint. It is, for certain, the result of overuse of the complex neurological and visual system that allows us to comprehend space.

Computer operators frequently say, "My eyes are so tired I just can't look at another word." Or they say, something like, "I feel I can't keep my eyelids open." Aside from indicating simple visual fatigue, eye tiredness can be a clue that cataracts (a clouding of the lens inside the eye) are starting to form. If cataracts are developing prior to the early forties, this can be focusing (technically, accommodative) fatigue. After age 40, focusing fatigue increases.

The special anti-glare filter I describe in the CRT-User Products section is completely effective at eliminating eye tiredness and eye fatigue.

Again I make the point: if your symptoms are severe, you should allow your eyes frequent breaks from your monitor, and you should have your eyes checked by an eye doctor.

✔ EYESTRAIN

"Eyestrain" is the word with which the CRT user describes vision problems experienced after having looked too long at a monitor. The user will say, "My eyes just feel strained." Sometimes the user will say, "They feel as if they are pulling," or "They feel as if they are being strained and pulled."

Eyestrain is the classic sign of overworked eyes — a condition resulting from not taking a few seconds every five minutes to glance away from a glaring monitor.

During times when you must think about what you are going to write or do next, and during computer response time or down time, you can rest your eyes. Take responsibility for your vision and how your eyes are going to feel for the rest of the day. A few hints:

- **When thinking, look away from the monitor.**
- **When waiting for the computer to respond, look away from the monitor.**
- **When waiting on down time, do eye exercises.**
- **Do not spend time reading or doing other near vision work such as knitting.**
- **Fix your focus on an object 25 to 30 feet away.**

Five seconds of looking away from the monitor when time avails is a perfect beginning to preventing eye problems.

Besides getting away from your monitor, try the following eye exercise.

- **Roll eyes around.**
- **Focus on the tip of your nose.**
- **Focus on a distant point — for example, 25 feet.**
- **Blink.**
- **Open your eyes, as if in surprise.**
- **Close your eyes and squeeze them tight.**
- **With eyelids closed, roll eyes around.**
- **Look up.**
- **Look down.**
- **Look left and right.**

An ancient Chinese remedy, used for thousands of years, is "palming." Cup your hands over eyes, making darkness. Darkness is restful to eyes.

The "20/20"™ anti-glare filter mentioned in the CRT User Products section has eliminated the eyestrain of any monitor user with whom I've worked.

✔ DIFFICULTY REFOCUSING

When distance vision isn't very good by day's end or when you have difficulty changing your focus from closeup to faraway, for example from reading your computer screen to identifing a coworker approaching the building from a distant parking lot, you have been too long at your monitor — you have been working for a longer period than your ocular system can tolerate. You need to rest your vision system. Get away from your monitor if possible. This is significant information to tell the eye doctor.

✔ DIFFICULTY FOCUSING COLOR

Difficulty focusing color is technically called "chromatic aberration." The eye does not focus all parts of the color spectrum at the same time. If you work at a color monitor occasionally, you might find your eyes tiring more often than they do when you work at a monochrome monitor. Reds and blues may seem blurred — with good reason, as they are less well focused than greens and blues, or black and white images. Monochrome monitors are often easier to read than most color monitors.

✔ BLURRED VISION

Eye tiredness and eyestrain seem to be followed by blurred vision.

The muscles of accommodation serve the purpose of focusing the lens so that you get what's called a "well-defined image" on the retina, which is at the inside back of your eye.

When the ocular system becomes overworked, eyes can no longer function effectively.

Because some monitors have what is referred to as "poor resolution," the ocular system cannot deliver a well-defined image to the retina. This causes the ciliary muscle of the eye to overwork in its effort to deliver a clear picture to the retina. It finally becomes too much work, and the retina image is not clear either near or afar.

- **Your eyes are exhausted. Leave your workstation for a minute or two.**
- **Reposition your monitor farther from your eyes.**
- **Do not read or watch television for several hours.**
- **Consider an anti-glare filter. The one described in the Resources section of this book is extremely effective in eliminating blurred vision.**

✓ EYE ACHE

Greatest in severity in my cataloging is eye ache. By this time, the condition has become painful.

- **At the front of the eye: Pupillary muscles become overworked, causing spasms.**
- **At the back of the eye: Ciliary muscles become overworked, causing spasms.**

When either condition exists, you have exhausted the ocular and neurological system that enables vision. Overused, exhausted muscles cramp. Prolonged muscle contraction leads to muscle spasms. *This is like the "charley horse" people get from overusing leg muscles, only it occurs in the eye muscles instead of in the leg muscles.* The 5,000-year-old Chinese technique of palming — cupping the hands over the eyes to create darkness — promotes relaxation of eye muscles and is always a good use of ten seconds of down time.

✔A HEAVENLY EYE REFRESHER

- **Get a thick washcloth.**
- **Cut it in half. Keep both halves in your bag or desk.**
- **Take half to the restroom.**
- **Drench the cloth in cold water.**
- **Squeeze it out slightly.**
- **Lie down, if the room allows. Otherwise, just lean your head back. (Remember toilet booths are available for privacy.)**
- **Place the cool, damp cloth over your eyelids.**
- **If ice cubes are available, place them atop the cloth.**
- **Rest for three to five minutes.**

This technique can be a real lifesaver to people with the worst of eye problems. Remember, handling the cloth too much (including wringing it out) will reduce its coolness.

After you have used the cloth, clean and wring it. Find a clean, isolated spot to store it at your desk. Be sure you've wrung adequately to prevent mildewing. Also, wash the cloth regularly.

✔BURNING EYES

Polluted air can cause burning eyes.

All manner of chemical fumes invade and pollute the workplace; building materials throw off naturally occurring radon; carpets have been treated with fire-proofing; furniture has been treated with anti-stain chemicals; photocopiers emit ozone. Seemingly innocent items in your purse — hair spray is one — throw off fumes that pollute the air.

Many of the newer buildings are hermetically sealed and recycle air rather than pull in fresh air from outside. You may be on the fifth floor, but you may well be inhaling the air pushed your way from Joe's smoky office on the eighth floor. Dirty air pushed from one part of the building to another is still dirty air.

Because many older buildings can have inefficient insulation, the air in them can change 20 times a day. Their inefficient insulation is a blessing in disguise. Sealed buildings, instead, simply store and recycle all pollution. The air might never be recycled.

Allergies and eye infections, which on their own can cause burning eyes, can worsen in the stale, dirty air of sealed buildings.

Air that is stale and depleted of negative ions can cause depression. If the air in your building seems stale and unfresh, if you feel depressed shortly after entering the building, I strongly suggest you get an ionizer and let it run 24 hours a day. As with other fashionable items, there are products on the market that do not do what they purport to do. In the last section, " CRT User Products," I provide information on the product I recommend.

✔ WATERY EYES

Watery eyes are generally a sign of stress — physical, emotional, or visual.

CRT users aren't the only people who experience this symptom. Remember the times you thought you couldn't cope for one more day with a particular stress? Remember when you went to bed and tears leaked from the corners of your eyes?

If you feel as though you can't make your "machinery" go another inch, another minute, you are overstressed and possibly even exhausted.

- **You're sitting too close to your monitor.**
- **Your monitor light is too bright.**
- **You need to do eye exercises.**
- **You need breaks away from your monitor.**

In short, your ocular system needs a rest. If you can take off work for a half-day, do so. Use the time to get several extra hours sleep. If you take the day off, don't make a path through the house doing all those stockpiled, backlogged chores. This can add to the problem. Take a relaxing bath, go for a walk, or listen to restful music with your eyes closed.

✔DRY EYES

It might not surprise you that during intense concentration, we stare. In staring, we forget to blink. When I work with individual computer operators, I take one of those yellow squares of Post-it notepaper and write on it:

Blink, Susan. BLINK.

And I place it at the top right corner of Susan's video display. Every time you blink, your eyes throw off the fluid needed to keep your eyeballs moist. When you concentrate intensely, forgetting to blink, your eyes become dry.

Low humidity can also cause dry eyes. CRTs emit heat. Heat dries the air and dry air takes moisture from the eyes. This can be especially troublesome if you wear contact lenses. You might find it useful to change to eyeglasses occasionally, if you can do so without experiencing problems with spectacle blur. You can also use eyedrops or artificial tears, preferably those recommended by an eye doctor.

✔ITCHY EYES

Dry eyes can become itchy because of inadequate humidity. Have building maintenance check room humidity for you. Humidity levels seem best when set between 40% and 60%.

Itchy eyes also can result from allergies to fumes emitted by various office machines. Synthetic materials used in upholstery and carpets also can cause itchy eyes. If you suspect allergies to be causing your problem, take heart. There are many anti-allergenic products on the market. Beware, *remember,* many of these same products can cause dry eye symptoms.

✔DRY AND ITCHY EYES

If your eyes are dry and itchy, you may be reacting to one or more elements in the air. Cigarette smoke, cosmetics and perfumes are but a few of the possible irritants. Numerous chemicals, such as listed above, invade and permeate the office.

If your office has a window, open it. Everyone needs and feels better with fresh air. If you wear contacts, take them out when you become aware of irritation.

✔EYE IRRITATION

Office equipment generally throws off heat, and heat dries the air. This lack of humidity can dry your eyes, allowing them to become irritated. Have the humidity level checked.

Irritated eyes can also be caused by static electricity thrown off by all equipment. Ion generators, or ionizers, can take excess positive ions out of the air. Read about them under "CRT User

Products" in the Resources section of this book.

Eyes can become irritated from wearing contacts too long. Have prescription eyeglasses available for use. Or try some of the liquid eye treatments from a pharmacy. Be careful to read package inserts for proper use.

✔EYE REDNESS

Fatigue and lack of adequate sleep can cause eye redness, as can prolonged use of contact lenses. If you consistently work long hours at a terminal, you might want to have single vision (not bifocal) eyeglasses measured for CRT use that you can change to them when your contacts become uncomfortable.

Other causes of eye redness include air pollution (smoke and dust) and other eye irritants. Persistent redness can indicate a more serious problem and need for a proper eye examination.

✔EYE SORENESS

If your eyes are over-sensitive to touch, if they feel tender, they may be inflamed, and might need to be checked by your eye doctor. This soreness also can be caused by sinus problems.

✔ONE-EYE ACHE

As mentioned in the PHYSICAL section under Headache Surrounding One Eye, the afflicted eye can be the weaker eye. When looking for this, I first check to see that the video display is "squared" with the user's eyes. The terminal that doesn't square with the user's eyes, can cause more pull on one eye than on the other, finally causing it to overwork and tire.

If the problem is not "squareness," then it can be exactly the opposite — that the terminal needs to be set off its square just a bit. By setting the display a half-inch or so closer to the weaker eye, it does just enough less work to make its task equal to that of the stronger eye.

Finally, the problem can be that one eye is somewhat more sensitive to light — the monitor's brilliance, in this case — than the other eye. In this case, the CRT user might find relief by positioning the side of the more sensitive eye to the dark area of the work area. In other words, if the right eye is more sensitive to brightness, the user would position the monitor so that any dark available in the room is to the user's right side. This often proves restful to the sensitive eye.

In conjunction, note that the reference material stand should be positioned with the above information in mind. If one eye is distinctly weaker than the other, place the copy holder so that it *favors* the weaker eye. If your right eye is clearly the weaker, position your paper holder to the right of the monitor. The distance from the left side of the monitor to the right eye is significantly greater than is the distance from the right side of the monitor to the right eye.

✔ FRONTAL EYE ACHE

Frontal eye ache is difficult to separate from frontal headache. These aches span the front surface of the eye or head area and discomfort is often overlapping. The cause is often eyebrow muscle tension from fighting glare and screen brightness. However, they can indicate visual problems that need attention:

- **farsightedness (hyperopia);**
- **astigmatism;**
- **ciliary muscle spasm;**
- **overuse of the convergence muscles; or,**
- **all of the above.**

If eliminating glare and adjusting for excessive brightness do not solve your problem, make an appointment with your eye doctor.

✔FLOATERS

Floaters are the amorphous, transparent spots that appear to be floating in your line of vision. They are usually seen when the eye is open and when observing a bright background (such as the sky or . . . hey, your monitor!). These semi-opaque particles are of various shapes and sizes and are suspended or floating in the fluids of the eye. When large enough, they cast shadows on the retina, thereby becoming visible.

No doubt you have noticed they disappear when you try to look at them. This is because they move as the eye moves.

Although these spots are usually normal, they can result from injury, disease, or degeneration of eye fluid. These conditions are generally detected during examination by an eye doctor.

Most spots are neither abnormal nor serious, but an eye doctor should be consulted if you experience them frequently.

✔AFTER-IMAGE

Known technically as the McCollic Phenomenon, "after-image" is a persisting sensation or image perceived after stimulus has been removed. Many CRT operators complain of a pink aura lasting several hours to several days after a long bout of CRT work. This bleached red after-image is caused by stimulation of the Hubbell-Wassell area of the visual cortex by the green phosphorescence of the letters created on the monitor.

> *When visual problems persist, see an eye doctor. At the end of this section of the book is a survey to be completed by you so that you provide your eye doctor most of the information he will need. Fill in the information while at your workstation and take it on your visit to the eye doctor. See the Vision Evaluation Form© at the end of this section.*

Optimizing Visual Health and Comfort

GLARE

Every day, the health, comfort, and productivity of CRT users is endangered. *Glare* coming off the monitor, by far the major complaint among CRT users, is a primary cause of numerous workstation problems — headache, in particular.

In fact, both headache *and* eye ache find their primary cause in the tension brought on by fighting glare. Further, this tension can radiate throughout the rest of the body. It then becomes a major contributing factor in blurred vision, burning eyes, watery eyes, neckache, and backache. This myriad of overlapping problems then causes exorbitant error rate, absenteeism, and turnover.

Glare results from improper setup of the CRT user's primary work tool, the monitor. Glare is caused by excessive overhead light; improper positioning of the display monitor; or by the intensity of light coming from the monitor itself. Each of these causes can be offset by one common solution — installation of an inside-mounted anti-glare filter.

✔EXCESSIVE OVERHEAD LIGHT

For best results, lighting at CRT workstations should be only about half that found in the average office. Excessive light at the monitor interferes with good vision and healthy eyes, and contributes to most eye problems. Eye problems range from tiredness and soreness to eyeball ache (front, back, and entire eyeball). Try these solutions to the problem of too much overhead light:

Turn down the overhead light. This may mean replacing 100-watt bulbs with 60-watt ones, or 75-watt bulbs with 40-watt ones, etc. (Typically, the lower, the better.)

Then, place a small (10- to 40-watt bulb) lamp to your side. Point the back of the lamp at you, and the front of it off to the side and *at* your reference material. Be certain the light from the lamp is not reflected in the screen.

Finally, tilt your monitor's face slightly downward (about five degrees). This will help keep the overhead lights off the screen.

✔IMPROPER CRT POSITIONING

In addition to avoiding overhead light, you will also want to minimize equivalent glare from the window. At every workstation, there is always a way to position the monitor to make the best of existing conditions at that particular location. Consider this position: The imaginary line between you and your monitor should run parallel with the line of the windows in the room. That is, when you sit at your monitor, the windows should be either to your left or to your right. Now with that idea in mind, you will see that it is a further improvement to angle your monitor a small bit off that parallel toward the windowless wall.

✔INTENSITY OF LIGHT COMING OFF MONITOR

The brightness of the monitor can intensify reflection of nearby images off the screen. This same brilliance greatly aggravates headache. There are two simple remedies to this problem.

Adjust the image brightness down until the light feels "soft" on your eyes. Be careful you are not now straining to read your display.

Install a mesh, inside-mounted anti-glare filter on your monitor. This will eliminate 90% of all glare problems. This very special filter (and *only* this type filter) generally eliminates headache, neckache, eyestrain, blurred vision, eyeball ache, and most other problems. In my experience, this has proven to be the most helpful solution to user visual discomfort. These filters are fine without the added features that some of them tout.

SUMMARY

PROBLEM	CAUSE	SOLUTION
GLARE	Excessive overhead light	Replace 100-watt bulbs with 75s; 75s with 60s, etc. Add small lamp; point at your reference material, from the side.
		Tilt monitor face downward. Install mesh "inside-mounted" anti-glare filter.
	Improper CRT position	Position monitor face parallel with window.
		Tilt display downward and slightly away from window.
		Install mesh "inside-mounted" anti-glare filter.
	Excessive monitor brightness	Adjust light downward.
		Install mesh "inside-mounted" anti-glare filter.

Courtesy of Mr. Joseph Arkin, Arkin Magazine Syndicate, 761 N.E. 180th St., North Miami Beach, FL 33162.

✔AVOIDING GLARE

Monitor brightness causes eyestrain and eye aches. Glare from other areas in the viewing area has the same effect. Following are pointers in eliminating glare.

- *Use an anti-glare screen.* See the CRT-User Products section at the end of this book for further information.
- *Make sure your monitor does not face a window.* If you must have a window directly at your back, rotate your desk an inch or two off its square. Do the same with your monitor.
- *Check the screen for glare and reflections.* White blouses are generally very troublesome, and you may want to wear soft- or dark-colored blouses.Jewelry and shiny picture frames and their glass can cause reflections. Remove jewelry until lunchtime, and reposition pictures.
- *Lower the overhead lighting level.* Try removing about half the fluorescent tubes. If overhead glare can't be eliminated, make an "awning" (a shield) for your monitor. Use a sheet of dark-colored cardboard. Tape it in place atop the monitor if the source of the offending glare is from above. If the source is a window to your side, tape the shield to the side of the monitor.
- *Remember to keep your monitor clean.* A film of dust makes the picture fuzzy.
- *Vertical venetian blinds allow for flexibility in casting off otherwise direct sunlight.*
- *Use a task light to illuminate your reference materials.* Be sure light points away from the monitor. A cone-shaped light that can be easily adjusted to your needs is best. Indirect lighting is ideal for computer work. When it isn't an option, parabolic louvers are an effective addition. Prisimatic louvers also diffuse light nicely. Full spectrum fluorescent lighting is preferred over standard fluorescent. Cool white deluxe is next in preference.
- *Never use a glass or plastic cover on your desk.*

And, in summary, these are the things that could be causing the glare problems:

- **light from windows**
- **white blouses**
- **bright, shiny jewelry**
- **desk items such as picture glass and frames**
- **overhead lighting**

And these are possible solutions:

- **an anti-glare screen**
- **rotating the desk and monitor**
- **choice of clothing and jewelry**
- **alteration of overhead lighting**
- **a custom-made "awning" for the monitor**
- **cleaning the monitor screen**
- **tasks lights**
- **vertical venetian blinds**
- **parabolic or prismatic louvers on lights**
- **choice of full-spectrum fluorescents**

Occasionally, CRT users complain that a shield gives the feeling of being "shut out" from the monitor, that they are struggling to "get in." The user has probably covered too much of the area, giving the feeling of restriction. If you make one of these shields, be sure its dimensions are only what is needed. It is generally adequate for the cardboard coming off the top of the monitor to extend a mere four or five inches toward the user.

> *Caution: Your monitor needs to breathe! Be sure not to block any ventilation slots. If you don't know what or where they are, ASK. Someone will know.*

Courtesy of Mr. Joseph Arkin, Arkin Magazine Syndicate, 761 N.E. 180th St., North Miami Beach, FL 33162

VISION EVALUATION FORM©

MARIN OPTOMETRIC GROUP

Dr. Howard A. Levenson and Dr. Robert B. Levine

1001 Grand Avenue

San Rafael, California 94901

415-453-3812

COMPUTER VISION REQUIREMENTS QUESTIONNAIRE

In order for the doctor to accurately assess your occupational vision needs and prescribe appropriate eyewear, the following information must be completed.

Distances:

1. Viewing distance to the computer screen is ________ inches.

2. Viewing distance to the computer keyboard is ______ inches.

3. Viewing distance to written material is ______ inches.

Direction:

1. The computer screen is: **above eye level**

eye level

below eye level

2. Written material is: **eye level**

below eye level

General Visual Information:

1. Time spent at computer: ______ hours per day.

2. Work performed while: sitting _____ other _____ (please describe). ________________________________

____

3. Lighting in work area (please describe). _____________

____

4. Background lighting (please describe). ______________

____

5. Brief job description: ___________________________

____

To comprehensively analyze your vision and visual needs at the VDT workstation, please completely fill out this questionnaire. **It is essential that you bring this questionnaire with you to the examination.** Some of this information will be used to simulate your work station.

Do you wear glasses while working at the VDT? Y N

(Bring them with you to the examination.)

How long have you been operating a VDT? ____________

How many hours/day do you work at a VDT? __________

Is your VDT work constant or intermittent? ___________

Do you take rest periods from VDT use? _____________

How often? ______________

TERMINAL

Terminal make and model: __________________________

Screen color. _____________________________________

Contrast — light on dark, or dark on light? ____________

Can contrast be reversed? ___________________________

Can brightness be adjusted? _________________________

Is the screen image clear and stable? _________________

WORK STATION DESIGN (MEASURE IN INCHES OR CENTIMETERS)

Chair height Adjustable? Y N

(floor to front of seat)

Keyboard height ________________________

(floor to keyboard)

Screen height ________________________

(floor to screen center)

Viewing distance ________________________

(eye to screen)

Is the screen titled? ________________________

Degree of tilt ________________________

Do you have an adjustable copy holder? Y N

Is the lighting on your copy material adjustable? Y N

Is the lighting on your copy material comfortable? Y N

Is the seat comfortable? Y N

Does the backrest provide firm support? Y N

Is the backrest adjustable? Y N

LIGHTING

Turn off your VDT:

Do you see any reflected light on the screen? Y N

Describe what reflection your see. ____________________

Turn on your VDT and bring some work on the screen.

Can you still see the reflections? Y N

Do the reflections interfere with the work? Y N

Do you use an anti-reflection screen on your VDT? Y N

Do you have a hood on your VDT? Y N

Look straight at your VDT screen.

Do you see any bright light sources with your peripheral vision (e.g. windows, overhead lights?) Y N

Describe the bright sources and their locations in your field of vision. If they are ceiling light fixtures, can you see the light tubes? Or is it nearly as bright as the light tube?

____

Do you see any bright reflections from the table surface, the computer equipment, or other nearby surfaces? Y N

If yes, describe: ____________________________________

Are you presently experiencing any of the following symptoms while working at or as the result of working at your VDT? Indicate with a check mark.

___ **Headaches**

___ **Blurred vision**

___ **Double vision**

___ **Eyestrain**

___ **Other, specify:** ________________________________

If you are experiencing any symptoms, please fill out the following:

How often do you experience these symptoms?

___ **Monthly**

___ **Weekly**

___ **Every other day**

___ **Every day**

How severe is the problem?

___ **Just noticeable**

___ **Can tolerate it**

___ **Very bothersome**

___ **Must seek immediate relief (e.g. aspirin)**

How long ago did the problem begin? ________________

When in the day does the problem occur? ____________

How long does the problem last? ____________________

Does anything help? ________________________________

____

Do you experience any neck, back, or arm strain while working at the VDT? ______________________________

____

HIT ANY KEY TO CONTINUE

STRESS

THE WORKSTATION AND STRESS PROBLEMS

For decades, the highest occupational stress level registered by National Institute of Occupational Safety and Health (NIOSH) was found among air traffic controllers. In 1981, however, a new study concluded that stress experienced by air traffic controllers has remained generally constant, but the highest occupational stress level is now found among CRT users.

In and of itself, stress isn't a bad thing. In fact, it is essential to life. It is phase one of the human alarm system, alerting us to impending danger or emergency. The problem, then, isn't stress. The problem is that the level of stress has exceeded all physical and emotional tolerance levels: we demand more stress toleration of the system than the system can tolerate.

Our overstressed systems, in turn, experience breakdown. Statistically, absenteeism, and turnover among CRT-using clerical workers are shocking. Absenteeism is reportedly 25% higher than among non-CRT-using clerical workers.

Stress, like the chicken and egg riddle, is cyclical: Causes and effects overlap. Management generally makes a major investment in computer equipment, and it must maximize its return; yet if display users do not take frequent breaks, they cannot maximize productivity. Where do we draw the line?

What work pattern maximizes productivity while assuring optimum employee health? These are inseparable concepts. If headache is severe enough to send an employee home, productivity falls precipitously. If an employee takes needless breaks, the problem with productivity is essentially the same.

Excess stress leads to illness, illness to absenteeism, absenteeism to turnover. As a computer operator, you extract payment from your health; management extracts payment from "the bottom line."

Can we altogether eliminate stress from the workplace? No, nor would we want to do so. Stress is a useful tool. Then can we bring it down to tolerable, healthy levels?

Let's start with a simple guide to good mental health.

The CRT User's Guide to Good Mental Health

Stress has a useful function in our lives. It keeps us alert to impending danger. Physical stresses, such as headache and noise, evoke biological reactions. Psychological stresses, such as feeling out of control and job insecurity, evoke psychological defenses. Some stresses evoke both types of reactions. When the body or the mind is overstressed, when the system experiences overload, we experience fatigue and exhaustion.

In this section, I give an elementary presentation of a very system that is both physiologically and psychologically complex. My purpose is to examine abuses of this complex system and to suggest effective remedies for thos abuses.

You'll find the program works for everyone, whether you are a CRT user, an office manager, a retired person, or a truck driver.

There are four major recommendations that I rely on for all stress problems, though the problems may not appear similar.

First, I cannot over emphasize the importance of work breaks. Get physically away from your monitor. By now you've gathered this is very important.

Second, Get some physical exercise. This, too, cannot be overemphasized.

Third, In this section, I add taking charge of your life. Too many of us sit back and become, in essence, victims. If you think you are a victim, you're right. If you think you deserve better, sit up, pay attention, take charge. Things *will* change. This entails a three-pronged approach. Mental housecleaning is essential to good mental health. Let go of bad thoughts, replacing them with good thoughts. Make things happen *for* you, not *to* you.

Fourth, clean living is as important to good mental health as it is to good physical health.

All of the above said, I reiterate the importance of regularly scheduled medical examinations for physical, visual, and mental health. You must see the proper medical authorities for what ails you.

Major Elements of Stress Problems

Stress is an extremely complex subject. A complete discussion of it is better presented by professionals who have defined and presented solutions in volume upon volume, much of it very good. Yet the number and severity of complaints among CRT users suggests something must be offered in this book.

Consider but a few symptoms: Irritability, isolation, fatigue, insomnia. Little wonder — there are as many symptoms as causes. Look at just one breakdown on stress.

One categorization of stress includes stresses we tolerate well and those we do not tolerate well. Both subdivide into low-grade and high-grade stresses.

Low-grade stresses we tolerate well include such events as the daily rhythms of showering, getting to work, and minding the child with sniffles. An example of a tolerable high-grade stress is playing tennis for several hours.

Examples of low-grade stresses we do *not* tolerate well include a dripping faucet, the chronic illness of a loved one, the moment the divorce becomes final. Examples of high-grade stresses we don't tolerate well include involvement in a serious accident, experiencing the death of a loved one, and wondering when job dismissal will occur.

It is obvious those stresses we do not tolerate well are also stresses we don't tolerate well for a long time.

Keep the above in mind while examining another breakdown of stress, all of them common among CRT users, all of them stresses we do not tolerate well.

PHYSICAL	VISUAL	CHEMICAL	EMOTIONAL
Overweight	**Need eye exam**	**Drugs**	**Job insecurity**
Discomfort	**Need glasses**	**Alcohol**	**Financial worry**
Pain	**Poor vision skills**	**Coffee**	**Family illness**
Fatigue	**Glare**	**Junk food**	**Dual work role of women at home and in the office**
Allergies		**Cigarettes**	

Further, CRT work compounds many forms of stress. Consider the following:

• **Physical stress:** CRT work requires a confining workstation design; the work itself requires sitting motionless; and management's investment in expensive computer equipment requires that maximum time shall be spent at the workstation.

• **Visual stress:** CRT work requires a visual fix on the monitor and non-stop concentration; consider this in context of the fascinating but not well-known fact that reading (an active brain response, consisting primarily of fast brain wave activity) and watching TV (a passive brain response, consisting primarily of slow brain wave activity) are controlled from opposite sides of the brain (H.E. Krugman, studying brain wave patterns for General Electric).

• **Chemical stress:** Being fixed all day at a workstation prevents the body's recuperative powers from taking over for even brief periods of the day.

• **Emotional stress:** A virtually endless array of conditions includes being isolated from co-workers by the need to be constantly monitoring one's CRT screen.

Following is another breakdown for examining categories of stress.

• **Environmental:** Noise; air pollution; low negative ionization; glare; ill-fitting workstations.

• **Work and job design:** Electronic monitoring; performance based on computer vs. human capacity; lack of control over work, no exercise of judgment; slow computer "response time;" boredom, career anxiety.

• **Socioeconomic:** Job insecurity; low pay; shiftwork.

The ultimate stress, exemplified above as stresses we do *not* tolerate well, is the "hopeless situation," the "dilemma" — neither way out seems tolerable; or, it seems no way out exists. Such is the stress of a full-time CRT user who experiences headache and eyestrain eight hours a day, who might be let go in the next cutback, and who provides the sole support for a small child in day school.

If you fall into the category of ultimate stress, if you feel like you "could just pop," you need to do something about your situation.

The major elements of minimizing CRT-user *stress* problems include:

- **taking charge of your life;**
- **identifying and eliminating the source of the problem.**

✔TAKE CHARGE OF YOUR LIFE

None of what follows is anything your company, your boss, or a friend can help you with. Yet stress among CRT users is serious indeed. No one knows that better than you. If you want to minimize it and its effect, you'll want to get started.

- **Don't be a blamer.**
- **Get some exercise.**
- **Take charge with good thoughts.**
- **Live a clean life.**

It is very important to recognize if you fall into the category of "blamer" (all your problems have their origin in someone else's behavior) or "victim" ("bad things just happen to me"). This kind of thinking — not being responsible, being out of control — will only intensify your problems. *You* are responsible. And so it must be. Otherwise, change cannot occur.

Pick a physical exercise to do at work (deep breathing, walking at noon), or one to do at home (before and after work, such as a 10-minute walk). Choose something you like to do. If you like to do things with others, ask a friend to join you. Whatever activity you choose, do it and do it regularly. Rain or shine. If you choose walking, you are not going to get hurt walking in the rain. Humidity removes oxygen from the air. If it's ghastly humid, breathing can become labored: slow your walk, but walk.

Mental housecleaning is essential to good mental health. Let go of bad thoughts. Take charge with good thoughts. Make things happen for you, not to you. There is material in books, on video, on tape cassettes — it's everywhere. Someone, somewhere has developed material useful to you. Just walk into any library or bookstore — the self-help shelves are loaded. Choose one or two of the books or tapes that to apply to your situation.

Finally, clean living is as important to good mental health as it is to good physical health. It goes without elaboration: Your body can tolerate only so much abuse. If you smoke a pack of cigarettes a day, consume fistfuls of junk food throughout the week, have several drinks after work, and indulge in "recreational" drugs over the weekend, is it any wonder you feel lethargic, zapped out? If your office building offers only a sealed ventilation system and there is a photocopier throwing ozone into the air, you are already experiencing excessive physical stress. Smoking, drinking, eating junk food, and using illicit drugs vastly compounds this existing stress.

These aspects of stress will not be elaborated on further. Many techniques for minimizing stress have been developed by

the professionals and the resulting information is available in health food stores, bookstores, video shops, libraries, and elsewhere. I urge you to find materials appropriate for you and follow through on some kind of program.

Taking charge combats the deleterious effects of working under physically and emotionally confining circumstances. *Please:*

- **Glance away from your monitor frequently.**
- **Take deep breaths.**
- **Get up and away from your monitor.**

Glancing away from your monitor frequently during thinking time or response time relieves your ocular system. Deep breathing is instrumental in lowering blood pressure and giving you a sense of tranquility. Standing up, even if you sit right back down, stretches muscles, puts your spine right, and promotes optimum blood flow. All of the above are antidotes than can — and should — be used all day long and at any time of the day.

Finally, whether or not you actually enjoy good health can be revealed only through examination by proper medical authorities. Follow the above tips and remember to see a doctor regularly for checkups.

IDENTIFYING AND ELIMINATING THE SOURCE OF THE PROBLEM

Look for symptoms of stress. They include cold hands and feet, high blood pressure, fatigue, insomnia, headache (including migraine). Stress parades as tension, dizziness, irritability, and stomach upset.

Identify the sources of your problem. *Take notes.* When you sense a "different" feeling, when you feel anxious, when your chest feels tight, when you feel you could scream: *Take note.* Keep a diary of the times of day and conditions associated with your stress. There is a good reason you feel the way you feel.

Talk to coworkers with whom you are friends. Do they share any of these feelings? Would getting together and discussing these feelings help? In getting together to chat, can you identify sources of common problems? Common solutions?

Do you feel you exercise no control over your job and the decisions being made? If so, how can you eliminate the problem of having no control? Can the job be redesigned? Can *you* redesign it? Can *you* influence someone else to redesign it? Perhaps *a group of you* can gain the support of management in developing more productive work routines and conditions.

Ask for the help and guidance of management. If *you* have problems, *they* have problems. Problems cost you your health; problems lessen management's profit; lost profit might have been your next pay raise. *Help management see what is everyone's loss.*

Create formats that can help you get to the source and solution of problems. For further solutions, see information in the Resource section of this book. The publication *9to5,* published by the National Association of Working Women, addresses the concerns of full-time computer users and provides information valuable to you in solving your problems.

Formats can make tackling office problems almost easy. You

will want to enumerate the problems according to category.

Recognize the importance of discussing your ideas with a supervisor, boss, or owner. If problems are serious enough that you feel you must take the initiative to correct matters, the problems are probably costing management a lot of money in lost productivity and high insurance premiums, in absenteeism and turnover — to say nothing of loss of goodwill of the employees. I urge you not to assume management doesn't care. It just isn't true. Again, getting employees to tell management the truth about aches and pains, stuffy rooms, air pollution, and related problems may be harder than getting management to listen. Employees assume that managers are cruel and unfeeling, and that things will forever be "us versus them." If you make that decision, it will be true. And it will remain true until you reverse that decision. Ask yourself how *you* would feel if *you* owned the company, and *your* employees were not telling *you* about problems impinging on their health and productivity. Everybody wins when you take charge and help bring about changes.

Environmental problems may be serious, but they are often the easiest sort of problems to address. Though they may be expensive to correct, their solutions are generally obvious.

Work and job design problems are major undertakings and entail work restructure, job rotation, and cross-training, to name but a few elements.

I encourage you to try resolving the socioeconomic problems. Go for it. Change what you can. In the meantime, until you've taken charge and laid out a plan of attack, let's look at what you can do right now to curtail your current problems.

Specific Stress Problems and Their Solutions

Results of my CRT-User Wellness Survey© indicate 43% of those surveyed experience fatigue frequently, most scoring three, four, or five on a scale of five, the most severe. Depression, insomnia, and boredom are other categories showing high scores.

Problems plaguing CRT operators probably vary little from problems plaguing the work population at large. They do, however, seem to be more severe. Solutions, therefore, are more important.

Solutions entail a "take charge" program. You are on your own. Nothing will change if you are not in charge. Anything can change once you decide you are in charge. So, out with the old "victim," in with the new "person in charge." Everything is possible, once *you* are in charge.

First: You'll want to develop your exercise program and your mental housecleaning program, and thoughts for improving your diet.

I'll say nothing further on these, except for diet: If you need to lose weight, I suggest you lighten up on your evening meal. Your level of metabolism follows your level of activity. That means that when you go to sleep, your metabolism slows. Eat a light meal before turning in for the night, and try to take that meal at least several hours before going to sleep. This approach avoids the agony of the 900-calorie daily diet. It is probably slower. But losing weight slowly is much more effective than adhering to killer diets. Close to 95% of people who crash diet regain their lost weight, and then some. This is because they are interfering with and confusing their metabolism.

Second: Chemical stresses call for little comment. Ingestion of these simply must be stopped; cutting down is second best. All those listed extract enormous premium from your well-being, but the worst is probably the sugar in junk food. Next time you reach for junk food, consider this: The "average" American's intake of sugar exceeds an equivalent two apple pies *daily.* That's right, the average American eats the sugar equivalent of *750 apple pies a year.* And don't think that you aren't pretty close to average unless you are a food purist, a nutrition buff, have your own garden, or are a vegetarian, and so on.

Third: Look at the emotional stresses, particularly those that relate directly to your work, your boss, and your company.

I suggest you create a format that makes tackling office problems easier. You will want to enumerate the problems according to category, and include a chart for solving each problem. *Include your supervisor or boss in the process. He or she cares.*

A final note: If you follow the suggestions in sections one and two of this book, and you still have physical and visual concerns, you might have overlooked the need for medical attention. Remember your "productivity breaks." (These are not to be confused with coffee breaks.) They need not be extended (a minute or two will do), nor away from your desk. Rotate tasks when possible.

Dr. Hayes, formerly corporate medical director at Burlington Industries and now with Sara Lee Corporation, structured job flow so that after 45 minutes at a monitor, the video operator went on a mail run. Terrific idea.He scheduled the user not only to be *away* from her screen, but to get moderate exercise *at the same time.* In four years of surveying users, those following his program were the only group ever to register few and insignificant complaints.

SOURCES AND SYMPTOMS OF STRESS

Now we'll look at some specific stress-related complaints and point out some probable causes and some solutions.

✔ FATIGUE

There are many causes of fatigue. Possible causes include excess positive ions in the air, boredom, overwork, overweight, allergies, depression, inadequate diet — the list is endless. Feeling anger and harboring resentments can be exhausting.

Chronic fatigue can result from emotional worry. Worse, it can indicate the body is struggling — but failing — in its effort to repair itself. If you experience chronic fatigue, I urge you to consult with your doctor.

In the Resources section at the end of this book, I mention negative ion generators. They change the air in the room, are energizing, produce a tranquilizing effect both physically and emotionally, and can be very reasonably priced.

If you experience *chronic* fatigue, I urge you to consider buying an ionizer. Actually, two ionizers. One for your workspace, and another for home. The correct product is generally very effective at relieving fatigue.

✔IRRITABILITY

Again, this is a problem with roots growing in many directions. Excess static electricity, emanating from the video display, can be the source. An ionizer can eliminate this problem. But the source of the problem might be your job.

Have you had your eyes examined? Possibly they do not work well together laterally and vertically, causing a high error rate, and subsequent irritability. Frustration brought on by poor job design can make you irritable. Problems at home can be carried over to the office. Determine what seems to be irritating you by noticing what you're doing, what you are thinking, when you seem irritable. Take steps to eliminate what's causing your problem.

✔ BOREDOM

Job design can be the greatest cause of boredom. It has been shown that work which calls for little thought and little decision making is not only boring but very stressful. This is especially true when the same work calls for keen concentration. You must look to supervisors to alleviate this problem. Ask about job rotation. Ask about cross-training in other tasks. Cross-training, long popular in Western Europe and Japan, generally results in soaring productivity increase. This results in increased self esteem and sense of satisfaction, and makes for a happy boss. Everyone wins. (Dredge up the cover story of the July 10, 1989, issue of *Business Week* on the subject of "teamwork" and pass it along to your supervisor.)

✔ DEPRESSION

Depression can be stress-related, and it, too, can have its cause in any number of places. The excess positive ions thrown off by the monitor are possibly the most serious cause of depression among CRT workers. Excess positive ions upset your electrical balance and can easily cause depression. Some people are more sensitive to this effect than others, but 40% of the population is generally thought to be sensitive to excess positive ions. The ionizer mentioned in the CRT User Products section can be enormously beneficial and a good solution.

Studies in several European countries have concluded that poor workload design is a major cause of depression and fatigue. If you believe this cause applies, perhaps you can help, with guidance from a supervisor, to redesign the workload.

Depression can be caused by job boredom. Could this be the problem? Would you enjoy your job more if things were somehow different? If yes, what "things"? What would you change? How? To whom do you need to direct your job analysis and request for restructure?

Be very careful not to overlook the value of talking to a psychologist, social worker or psychiatrist. I'm sure you've heard the line about seeing a bone doctor if you have broken a bone, or an eye doctor if you've gouged an eye. Don't be caught among those who are still quick to pooh-pooh the effectiveness of talking out problems with those who have spent years trying to develop the objectivity it takes to be a good "sounding board" for others.

✔ INSOMNIA

Insomnia can result from stress. It should be discussed with the company nurse or another medical person, and immediately. You cannot go without proper rest. I suspect insomnia is more prevalent among those hypersensitive to excess positive ions. If you have no emotional reason for insomnia, determine whether you experience it on weekend nights, when you have been away from your monitor, less than on than on weekday nights.

✔ NOISE

Mary McQueen, an anti-noise pollution activist working in Texarkana, Texas, speaks of the toll noise takes on our physical and emotional health and the preventive measures we can take to avoid it. According to McQueen, noise does not have to be loud enough to cause hearing impairment to do harm. Excessive, unwanted noise can increase blood pressure, accelerate heart rate, increase adrenaline flow, weaken the immune system, and cause the pupils of the eyes to dilate. It can result in headache, fatigue, irritability, and anxiety and it can interfere with your ability to concentrate and learn. Irritating noise can reduce worker productivity and accuracy. Reduce noise levels in offices through the use of floor carpenting, acoustical enclosures for printers, rubber pads placed under noise-producing equipment, desks made of wood rather than metal, sound-absorbing wall coverings, and acoustical dividers between work stations.

If management does not purchase noise-reducing products, workers can take some inexpensive steps. Place thick rubber pads or pieces of carpet (cleaned and aired to remove noxious chemicals) under noisy machines. When possible, locate such machines away from corners whence noise reverberates. As a last resort, wear ear plugs. (Make sure they are clean). Ear plugs can be found in the sporting goods departments of discount stores, drug stores, industrial supply stores, gun shops, and hardware stores.

If you work in a noisy office, for your health's sake allow your ears a rest period when you return home. Avoid turning on the television or stereo for awhile and play them at moderate volumes when you do. Avoid running several noisy appliances at the same time.

Getting a good night's sleep will help you feel better and be a better worker. This may be difficult if you live in a noisy neighborhood. Some people try to mask intrusive sounds with fans or machines called sound conditioners. These machines produce a soothing, steady synthesized sound of falling rain, waterfall, surf, or rushing air. They are not effective at masking loud noise, and there are those who would debate the merits of adding sound to sound. Nevertheless, you may find one of these machines generally beneficial. If you cannot find one of these machines at a medical supply store, you can order one from the Sears, Roebuck and Company Health Care catalogue.

✔LOW PAY

CRT users often approach me on the subject of personal finances. Many feel their pay isn't adequate. Yet, when I ask specific questions about their living expenses — what they are, how they add up — I get answers that are at best vague.

This happens often enough that I thought a standard budgeting procedure might prove useful to you.

CRT-USER BUDGET FORM A

Budget Form A is for those who have no sense at all of where their money goes. It is a guide for tracking your every penny of out-go. *Photocopy and carry it with you.* For two months. I really mean carry it with you, and for two months. You will be amazed at how many nickels, dimes, quarters, and dollars you spend without aforethought. These are what's killing you. Those two dollars pushed into the cigarette machine plus the 50 cents in the candy machine add up to $2.50 a day. Multiply that by just 20 or more days a month, and you're looking at $50 dollars a month you had no idea you were spending. If you saved it instead, you'd have the first half of your ticket to the Caribbean by year's end. And if you saved it for two years, you'd have your return flight paid. Think two years is a long time to wait? When's the last time you've been to the Caribbean?

Start paying attention — which need not mean penalizing yourself. Instead it may mean giving yourself an island adventure, a new camera, membership in a health spa, or something else that you have consciously chosen to enrich your life. Do it by moving from Budget Form A to Budget Form B.

CRT-USER BUDGET FORM B

This form is for those who already have some sense of where their money is going but haven't put it down in black and white. I think it will give you a sense of where it all really goes.

When you reach this stage, remember to include, when applicable, pay data from another job or that of your spouse.

Some helpful numbers: One school of thought holds that you should take 10% off the top of your net pay and put it directly into savings; also, that not more than 25% of your pay should go to housing and utilities. If these, and other, goals are currently not possible, you might want to give your numbers a hard look.

CRT-USER BUDGET FORM A: Tracking monthly expenditures by the day.

	1	2	3	4	5	6	7	8	9	10	11	12	13	14	15
HOUSING															
Rent or mortgage															
Taxes/insurance															
Repairs															
Other															
Sub/Total housing															
UTILITIES															
Water															
Gas															
Electricity															
Sub/Total utilities															
PUBLIC TRANSPORTATION															
Bus															
Subway															
Taxi															
Other															
Sub/Total public transp.															
PERSONAL TRANSPORTATION															
Loan payment															
Insurance															
Maintenance/repairs															
Fuel															
Sub/Total personal transp.															
FOOD															
Expense															
Expense															
Expense															
Sub/Total food															
MEDICAL															
Expense															
Expense															
Sub/Total medical															
ENTERTAINMENT															
Expense															
Expense															
Sub/Total entertainment															
OTHER															
Expense															
Expense															
Sub/Total other															
TOTAL DAILY EXPENDITURES PER MONTH															

16	17	18	19	20	21	22	23	24	25	26	27	28	29	30	31	Total Monthly Expenditure
																*

***Whether you add down the last column or across the bottom line, this block should total to the same amount.**

CRT-USER BUDGET FORM A1

TRACKING ANNUAL ADDITIONAL INCOME ON A MONTHLY BASIS

ADDITIONAL INCOME	JAN	FEB	MAR	APR	MAY	JUN	JUL	AUG	SEP	OCT	NOV	DEC	TOTAL
Interest Income													
Dividend Income													
Gift Income													
Other Income													
Other Income													
Other Income													
Total Additional Income													

CRT-USER BUDGET FORM A2

TRACKING ANNUAL EXPENDITURES ON A MONTHLY BASIS

LIVING EXPENSES	JAN	FEB	MAR	APR	MAY	JUN	JUL	AUG	SEP	OCT	NOV	DEC	TOTAL
Housing													
Utilities													
Transportation													
Public													
Private													
Food													
Medical													
Entertainment													
Other													
Other													
Other													
Other													
Other													
Total Additional Expenditures													

CRT-USER BUDGET FORM B

ESTIMATING ANNUAL FUNDS AVAILABLE FOR SAVINGS AND INVESTMENT AFTER CALCULATING ALL ADDITIONS AND DEDUCTIONS TO INCOME

ANNUAL GROSS PAY (Enter here) $______

Deductions from Annual Gross Pay:

FICA ______
Federal Income tax ______
State Taxes ______
Health Insurance ______
Retirement ______
Other ______
Sub/Total, Deductions <__________>

ANNUAL NET PAY (Gross pay minus deductions) $______

ANNUAL OTHER INCOME

(Amounts carried forward from Budget Form B1)

Interest Income ______
Dividend Income ______
Gift Income ______
Other ______
Other ______
Sub/Total, Additional Income (total of above) +__________

ANNUAL EXPENDABLE INCOME

(Net pay plus additional income) $______

LIVING EXPENSES

(Amounts carried forward from Budget Form B2)

Housing ______
Utilities ______
Transportation ______
Food ______
Medical ______
Entertainment ______
Other ______
Sub/Total, Living Expenses (total of above) <________>

TOTAL FUNDS AVAILABLE FOR SAVINGS AND INVESTMENT

(Expendable income minus living expenses) $______

✔JOB DESIGN AND CONTENT

As CRT work hasn't progressed much beyond the stage of mechanization for the bulk of computer workers, there is much room for improvement in job design and job content. And though CRT workers seem generally to like their work, the less mechanical their jobs are, the greater the satisfaction they express with their work.

If you find your work tiresome, boring, or dissatisfying, spend some time analyzing the reasons for your feelings. How could your workload be changed so as to make your work more satisfying?

In general, full-time CRT users seem to find piece work more fatiguing and less satisfying than work compensated at an hourly rate. Further, fatigue seems to decrease with increase in diversity and complexity of the work done. What can you do to help make your work more diverse, more interesting? Can you add one or two of your coworkers' tasks to your own and come up with a new job assignment? One in which you can share and rotate tasks?

✔CAREER ANXIETY

Most of the full-time computer workers I consult with seem to like their work. Among many employees, however, there are work-related problems ("My eyes are fatigued—") that create anxiety ("Dare I leave my computer for two minutes?" "Will I be thought a trouble maker? Lose a pay raise? Lose my job?")

These feelings seem to fall into three basic categories.

First, there are those who fear that computerization will one day eliminate their jobs. To them I say, "Get all the training you possibly can." Learn every new skill, take every opportunity available to you. And by the way, don't forget that it's now going on thirty years that everyone's been talking about how computers were going to eliminate all the jobs the world has to offer. Yet today, even though we are now into the Era of the Robot, it simply hasn't even begun to happen. At worst, you will probably move into another similar job — such as making robots to do the job you used to do.

Second, there are those who, because they love to effect change, would like to move into management. They love their jobs but want to see them done differently, better; and they think they could help make that happen if they "joined the management team." Remember that "the team" is always looking for someone just like you. Go talk to them. Lay out a plan for the changes you feel would make things better and more efficient; outline what you can do for the company. Then ask someone to hear you out. Remember that management needs you. There's no way they want to lose a good employee, a far-thinking person, someone with a vision. The ball's in your court.

Finally, in between these two positions is someone who feels she is on a dead-end track, but doesn't understand why, and has no solutions. Be not dismayed. Go to your bosses. Tell them you have no solutions. This does not diminish your problem. You are a good and devoted employee, yet you feel you are going down the road that says *Detour.* What do they suggest? Do they have some kind of counselling? (The answer, likely, is Yes.) Can you get some other kind of training? (This answer, too, is likely to be Yes.)

Believe me, if your work and attendance records are good, even if you only recently have "turned over a new leaf," your company wants to know if something is troubling you, and what it will take to keep you.

Optimizing Mental Health and Comfort: Excercise

Optimum posture is one solution to the problems brought on by constant sitting demands. Another solution is exercise — exercise that takes the spine through a normal range of motion and integrates nerve, muscle, bone, and ligament movement.

Like any "chain-like" structure, the spine is not designed to hold a particular posture indefinitely. Muscle fatigue, ligamentous pain, or nerve entrapment will alert the sitter to the need for movement.

The most beneficial form of movement is exercise. In fact, one school of thought is that exercise can be more important than the food one eats. That notion is based on the fact that exercise speeds blood through the body, and blood in turn provides oxygen and nutrients to the cells — and, in one sense, each of us is basically nothing more or less than an aggregation of approximately 100 trillion cells.

Thus it is suggested that you exercise daily. No matter what kind of exercise you choose, spend a few minutes a day doing it. Exercise causes you to sleep better at night, thereby evoking a sense of well-being on awakening. You will be surprised at how much more alert you are. The exercise that rushes oxygen and nutrients through your body rushes oxygen and nutrients to the brain specifically. So not only does your health benefit, but the quality of your work improves.

David A. Thompson, Ph.D., of the Terman Engineering Center at Stanford University, advocates taking exercise breaks. Physical exercise designed to be timely and relevant to the specific job proved so successful that the companies in his study subsequently introduced *paid* exercise breaks for CRT users. Dr. Thompson also encourages use of the 20- to 30-second microbreak to stretch and flex the affected muscles. Exercise is especially important to hands and wrists which, now working so hard, desperately need fresh blood. Without exercise, capillaries become locked in place and circulation is reduced. (In Dr. Thompson's study, workmen's compensation claims fell to practically none after introduction of the exercise program. The number of items processed by the bank worker subjects in one study initially increased 50-60% before settling to a slightly lower level. The number of customer checks waiting to be deposited into interest-bearing accounts was reduced drastically. And of course, workmens' compensation costs fell.)

✔ TWO NOTES OF CAUTION

First, most experts agree that you should stretch your way into all exercise. Never jump suddenly into an exercise, whether touching toes, jogging, twisting the upper body, or any other maximum-movement motion.

Remember that your muscles have been in the same cramped position for hours. They are jammed with waste products and blood, the nerves in the muscles are squeezed, and the joints involved with these muscles are swollen and stiff. Sudden, violent, or exaggerated movements under these conditions can be harmful.

Remember, though we rarely see behind the scenes, amateur and professional athletes spend at least half an hour warming up before each event.

Several important points about stretching are:

- **Never stretch a painful joint or muscle. You could tear it or cause arthritis to form.**
- **Stretch only to the point of resistance, never to the point of intense discomfort.**
- **Never bounce while in a stretched position. Tight muscles can be torn easily.**

✔ BREATHING AND EXCERCISE

A suggestion for maximizing benefits derived from exercise: *practice breathing that is in harmony with what your body is doing.*

- **Inhale while stretching**
- **Exhale when contracting**

Inhale when stretching muscles into expansive positions. Example: Inhale deeply and slowly as you move your hands from out to an extended position at your sides, then to a position above your head. The time it takes to make this inhalation should equal the time it takes to move the hands and arms through this full motion.

Exhale when contracting muscles back to normal resting positions. Example: Exhale fully and slowly as you move your hands from above your head to an extended position at your sides and back to a hipside resting position. The time it takes to make this exhalation should equal the time it takes to move the hands from above the head a hipside position.

Breathing that is harmonious with body movement brings many benefits, including:

- **strengthening your spine:**
- **making long, slender muscles and a lovely body:**
- **making your entire body supple; and**
- **lowering blood pressure.**

Devote 10-12 minutes in the morning to simple stretching movements, and another 10-12 minutes in the evening, and I guarantee you will feel like a new person in 10-12 days. And just to help you get started right now, on the next page are examples of a few simple stretches. If you take three minutes right now, you'll get a good idea of what this will do for you.

On your mark, get set . . .
. . . Go.

1. Place your feet 12-15 inches apart.

2. While inhaling slowly and deeply, slowly raise your hands above your head.

3. Hold this position. Feel your lungs fill with oxygen.

4. Now, slowly bend forward from the waist *while exhaling slowly and fully,* until you form about a 90-degree angle. Your hands should be level with your head.

5. *Continue exhaling — slowly.*

6. Now go on down and touch the floor. (Can't? That's another reason you ought to be doing this.)

7. Now, *while inhaling slowly,* move back to your standing position and drop your arms naturally to your sides.

8. Let your head fall forward.

9. Standing in place, take a deep breath and exhale slowly.

10. Lift your head and assume a normal standing position.

Start from the beginning and do this stretch one more time.

Here is the opposite movement.

1. Keep standing with your feet 12-15 inches apart. *While inhaling slowly and deeply,* slowly raise your hands above your head again.

2. *Continue inhaling.*

3. Now, *while beginning to exhale slowly,* arch your back slightly, bending back as far as possible. Feel the tug on your tummy muscles.

4. When you can exhale no further, inhale, and come back up to your standing position.

5. Drop your arms naturally to your sides, and let your head fall forward.

6. *Standing in place, take a deep breath and exhale slowly.*

7. Lift your head and assume a normal standing position.

Repeat exercise.

If you did exercise #1 twice, and #2 twice, You are now four steps closer to touching your toes. You probably feel considerably more relaxed. You have done something very good for your health, and for all of this, you have probably spent only 90 seconds — or .17% of the approximate 54,000 waking seconds (15 hours) available to you today.

The next exercise is just as simple and will also feel great.

1. Position your feet about 30-40 inches apart.

2. *While inhaling slowly and deeply,* extend your arms outward to both sides so that arms and shoulders draw a straight line from left to right.

3. Now, keeping your left arm generally straight with your shoulder, *exhale slowly and fully* as you slowly bend to your right side. Continue to bend, sliding your right arm down toward your right foot.

4. When you complete exhaling, *start inhaling,* as you move back into your standing-with-arms-straight-out position.

5. Hold this position (arms out), and *exhale fully.*

6. *Now inhale,* and repeat the same stretch toward the left.

7. Again, when you have fully exhaled, *start inhaling,* and return to normal standing position.

8. Let your arms drop naturally to your sides and let your head fall forward.

Adding another 90 seconds or so to your exercise routine, you have now spent about three minutes, or just over 3% of your waking hours in an activity that will make you feel physically relaxed and mentally alert.

How do you feel?

Are your neck muscles looser? Is you back more relaxed? Is your breathing slower? Are you naturally breathing more deeply?

This is how simple it is.

The choice is yours.

STRESS EVALUATION FORM©

PROBLEM	POSSIBLE CAUSES	POSSIBLE SOLUTIONS	WHO CAN HELP	SUPERIORS TO INCLUDE IN SOLUTION
Environment				
Noise				
Air pollution				
Stuffy air				
Glare				
Poor workstation design				
Ill-fitting chairs				
Work & Job Design				
Electronic monitoring				
Rapid pacing				
Performance based on computer vs. human capacity				
Lack of control over work				
No chance to exercise judgement				
Slow computer response time				
Boredom				
Career anxiety				
Socioeconomic				
Job insecurity				
Low pay				
Shiftwork				

Resources

RESOURCES

During the several years I have worked with CRT users, I have discovered products that were recognized as instrumental to getting the job done and essential to good health. The following information introduces products and publications that are generally inexpensive, useful, and easy to obtain, and organizations that can provide information in your field of interest. Keep in mind that suppliers may give considerable quantity discounts if they can ship to one address only. If your fellow CRT users join you in ordering or if your supervisor orders for the entire section or division, you will find the suppliers I've listed most agreeable to discounting their products and willing to help in any way. Be sure to allow at least four weeks for delivery.

No quid pro quo, not by any name — no commissions, no proceeds, no kickbacks, no referrals — has been arranged for mention of any of the following products, services, or publications.

CRT-USER PRODUCTS

ANTI-GLARE FILTER

Anti-Glare Filter

CRT Services, Inc.

P. O. Box 1525

Kerrville, TX 78029-1525

In the first edition of my book, I went on at length about this product. It is, simply, amazing. I've seen it reverse — not credible in the minds of others — what was otherwise considered permanent vision deterioration.

Nothing can ever deter my promoting this product.

Alas, as we go to press with this latest edition, this company is in the process of changing hands. Because I couldn't bear not to have an address listed, I called the Canadian company with which I was so closely affiliated for several years (the company listed in the earlier edition of my book) and asked if they would ship me stock of their most commonly requested anti-glare filters, allowing me to fill orders until the issue of ownership was settled.

Thus, if you want one of these screens, send a postcard to my address, as listed above, and I shall have someone contact you regarding payment and other specifics.

It was quite by accident that this extraordinary product became my introduction to the world of computer ergonomics.

No anti-glare screen on the market compares to the 20/20™ product which I refer to as "resolution-correcting." Technicians firmly assert that one cannot "correct a monitor's resolution" — the picture is clear, fuzzy, or something in between. Technically, this is correct.

Do I disagree with the authorities?

The answer is No. I call the filter resolution-correcting because *it gives the perception* of correcting resolution, and this seems to be what matters to the focus mechanism of the eye. If the retina of the eye receives a "well-defined image," the focusing act has been completed. Having worked with thousands of CRT users, I developed hypotheses for the effectiveness of this filter. I finally decided, correctly or not, that monitor brightness causes headache; monitor fuzziness causes eyestrain. Putting *any* anti-glare screen on a monitor blocks the brilliance of the monitor's light, thereby stopping headache. Putting *any* anti-glare product on a monitor, however, blurs the picture the eye sees, thereby worsening eyestrain.

If use of the 20/20™ filter eliminates eyestrain, then the mechanics of the eye must have been favorably affected. In my research, the CRT user, armed only with this filter, halts:

- **most headache (except headache caused by vision problems or other disorders needing medical attention);**
- **neckache resulting from headache;**
- **eye problems (except those requiring medical attention);**
- **most fatigue, depression, and irritability.**

If you are a full-time computer user, you know one person can have all the above problems. It may seem to be a sweeping statement to tell you that a special anti-glare filter alone could eliminate most of those problems, but this is my experience. This filter remedies visual problems that do not require medical attention and relieves the physical-and stress-related problems exacerbated by sitting all day.

Because in 95% of the cases this product stops serious eyestrain, blurred vision, and eyeball ache, I hypothesize that it creates a well-defined image ready for interpretation by the brain, freeing the ciliary muscle from its ordinary task of focusing the lens to develop the image required for reading. Succinctly, the filter does the work that the brain otherwise causes the ciliary muscle to do.

I think I have seen every type of anti-glare filter on the market, including those which *look* similar to the one Ken Hopper offers. The uniqueness of his product is the extremely fine, very expensive, nylon micromesh cloth. Filters using thicker cloth are not equally effective in relieving eyestrain; in fact, there's evidence they intensify eyestrain.

Note: In my testing so far, I have found one type of person who cannot use this product — the person who has severe motion sickness. Please note the word severe. The weave of the cloth against the monitor's lettering seems to evoke a sensation of movement. This sensation nauseates the viewer who is strongly susceptible to motion sickness.

People with mild motion sickness seem to adapt, if they push their monitors a bit farther from their eyes. The "front mount" not only seems the product of choice for users susceptible to motion sickness, but their eyes do not seem to tire from its use.

CHAIRS

Carol Hunter

Industrial Biomechanics of North Carolina

P. O. Box 526

Oak Ridge, NC 27310

1-919-643-7707, telephone

Industrial Biomechanics specializes in back problems, and has very useful information on name brand chairs.

Ms. Hunter has made an in-depth study of chairs, categorizing them according to features: pan size, back size, ease of adjustability, and so on. (For instance, the "three-finger test," mentioned in the chair information, was pinched from one of her lectures.)

For instance, if the pan of a chair is particularly deep, that is, if it is long from buttocks to knee, and your legs are short from buttocks to knee, there's simply no point, assuming the purchase is for you, in your looking at that particular (name brand) chair.

This is extremely important and useful information. Your homework has been done for you. Managers, purchasing agents, supervisors of VDT users: If you're in the market for new chairs, I can only urge you to see the significance of the differing dimensions of chairs, and contact Ms. Hunter for this invaluable information.

If you will call, Industrial Biomechanics will send you a brochure that provides, in chart form, clear concepts in analyzing chair function and value, so you will know, when shopping, what chair is right for you from the outset.

Coby Dietrick
Relax the Back Store
5800 Broadway, Suite 101
San Antonio, TX 78209
1-210-822-1228, telephone
1-210-822-4564, fax

It's great fun, meeting people in this business. Computer ergonomics is a quite a new field, and most everyone in it is an entrepreneur or a maverick. We're all so excited about the new things we're learning and doing that how we spend our day is really fun and rewarding.

Coby Dietrick called me one day from San Antonio. He had seen my book and wanted to discuss computer work, workstations, back problems, chairs, and so many subjects.

So we talked for quite some time.

Turns out, Mr. Dietrick, a former NBA basketball player, owner of a chair store in San Antonio, has become intrigued by sitting — in all its aspects — and has developed a fascinating philosophy about chairs as tools and how to use these tools; for example, sharing the workload among the body's many different sets of muscles.

Call Mr. Dietrick — he'll weave you a Philosophy of Chairs and Sitting so intriguing that you'll spend the entire afternoon listening to him. He consults to businesses interested in the uniqueness of the human body, its plight in today's workplace, the subsequent cost of this to management, and how to make all this composit uniqueness work to everyone's benefit.

Nada Chair

2012 Como Avenue, SE

Minneapolis, MN 55414

1-800-722-2587, toll free

"This is not a chair," Nada is quick to tell you. It is further amusing that they tell you this 13-ounce (less than one pound) package that parades as a chair "includes no frame, legs or seat."

This is a terrific product for anyone who doesn't intend to buy a chair, yet needs reliable back support.

The Nada is a foam pad covered with canvaslike cloth designed to fit across the lower back. Straps extend to and loop round the knees, where a buckle comes in to hold these adjustable-length straps together.

The Nada fits snugly while you are sitting, but simply drops to the floor when you stand up. And then it all tucks up and folds into a portable pack with handle straps, so you can carry it wherever you are going: fishing, a football game, to read or meditate.

At $39.95, it's a viable alternative to a new chair whether you're on a low budget or simply not sitting the number of hours that might seem necessary before investing in a good-quality chair.

At a computer show in Dallas I was given a Nada chair to test personally, and — while acknowledging that I have a stand-up workstation — when I have reason to sit for any stretch, I can say it is amazingly useful. And, yes, I carry mine with me on any kind of travel.

CONE LIGHTS

Several types of cone lights are available. One of them stands on the desk; another clamps onto the side of the desk. Arms can be flexible or fixed.

You can buy such a lamp at K mart, Wal-Mart, Radio Shack, or office stores such as OfficeMax and Office Depot. The cost is $8 to $35, depending on options and workmanship.

IONIZERS

John Proynoff

Quantum Ecologic Company

P. O. Box 60036

Phoenix, AZ 85082

602-956-6174

602-957-7137, fax

A very readable book, *The Ion Effect* by Fred Soyka (New York: Dutton, 1977), explains the devastating effect which excess positive ions can have on some of us. Mr. Soyka is a Canadian who, stationed in Switzerland as an employee of IBM, met head-on with excess positive ions. If the book is not available at your library, it is probably at a health food store for $5. If you find that you feel "peculiar" or "disconnected" after a night's sleep in an air-conditioned room, or if you are restless in your hermetically sealed office, you might be hypersensitive to excess positive ions. If you are having the "video blahs," as some people call them, then this book might be for you. It won't change the way your body reacts to excess positive ions, but it will provide the information you need to change your life if you don't like the discomfort, fatigue, restlessness, and occasional headache associated with excess positive ions.

About ten years ago, I found this out for myself. After several visits to a doctor, I confessed to being baffled at how tranquil I felt on leaving his office. I asked what that "peculiar thing" in the corner was, always humming its gentle sound. He said it was an ionizer — an ion generator.

A friend of mine was seeing the same doctor, and his response was the same as mine. We agreed that we left the doctor's office on "cloud nine." My friend bought an ionizer. He once left it with me while he was on vacation. Its effect on me was marked. For the first time in my life I could sit and read without springing up for something every five minutes. In fact, I could read for an hour or two without interruption.

Not everyone is sensitive to excess positive ions, but apparently 30% to 40% of the population is. If you are among that number, the problem can be unsettling. Solving this problem is not particularly expensive. A spare $200 can change your life. Perhaps you can get the company to consider buying the larger version, which costs about $500. It will help everyone in the workroom. Or perhaps everyone would like to pitch in on the expense. The change is remarkable.

Beware — many products on the market purport to do what the ionizer does, but only the ionizer puts billions of negative ions (the "good guys") in the air. Negative ions connect with and remove positive ions from the air, leaving excess negative ions to restore your electric balance and make you feel refreshed and energized. An ionizer also can stop skin rashes caused by excess positive ions.

The correct type of ionizer depends on the cubic footage of the room where the ionizer will be located. Be certain before you call about the product that you know the measurement of your office space (length, width, and height).

John Proynoff will tell you everything you need to know. He is a professional who will sell you exactly what you need — nothing more, nothing less.

FURNITURE

Anthro Technology Furniture

3221 NW Yeon Street

Portland, OR 97210

1-800-325-3841, toll free

1-800-325-0045, toll free fax

1-800-325-0259, TDD

How many companies can you think of that are up to date enough to have a TDD number?

And, yes, it is indicative of the way they think at Anthro.

Going through Anthro's catalogue is like going to a hardware store. Know the feeling? It's fun, and it's intriguing.

With all their mix-and-match products, buying from Anthro can be reminiscent of playing with Tinker Toys; on the other hand, this is indeed a serious catalogue. What they offer you is the ability to put together a workstation in just about any configuration you would like. That means the shapes are esthetically of your chosing and the dimensions are suited ergonomically to your physical needs.

Anthro doesn't pretend to be inexpensive. It is instead, to quote the catalogue, "fanatical about the quality of our materials and craftsmanship. You'll feel it in our smooth, heavy tubing, and our thick, blemish-free shelves. You'll be delighted at the tight fit when you assemble it *with the tools we provide.*"

My emphasis on tools. Anyone else you know send you tools?

This company is amazing: It offers you a lifetime warranty (yes, that's the life of the product!); has a 100-day risk-free policy (just send back whatever you don't need); and typically ships within twenty-four hours. Anthro's products pass the stringent testing of an independent lab, which tests results they are happy to share with you.

Incredibly, Anthro offers a "Touch and Feel Kit." If you want a sample of the quality of their products, just ask. Is there a charge? Yes. Is it for naught? No; the cost of the kit is applied toward your purchase.

Anything else unusual about this company? In fact, if you donate your old computer workstation to a recognized charitable organization, Anthro will take $50 off the price of your new AnthroCart.

In Anthro's innovative approach to practical ergonomics, the company is developing a line of books (mine among them). Later, they plan to include other ergonomic guidelines among their offerings.

KEYBOARDS

The MALTRON Keyboard

Stephen W. Hobday

PCD Maltron Ltd

15 Orchard Lane

East Molesey

Surrey KT8 0BN England

081-398-3265, telephone

"The uneven stretches caused by the diagonal slope of the rows of keys on [the standard] Qwerty [keyboard] result in uneven reach and distance movements, and this, together with the letter layout which reinforces language confusions and induces errors, adds to learning difficulties and training time. Of course, there are many highly skilled and accurate keyboard operators. They are only a small proportion of the total number of people who learn to use a keyboard, and their skill has taken longer to achieve and required greater effort. These difficulties all add to the cost of providing training both in our educational and training establishments, and in industry."

With these words, Lillian Malt, a veteran keyboard trainer of some twenty years, advised Stephen Hobday, engineer on the lookout for a project, that a new and very different keyboard was desperately needed.

Mrs. Malt and Mr. Hobday trace the origin of the Qwerty keyboard layout to a problem typists encountered with the older (circa-1862) Scholes keyboard. The bars of the Scholes keyboard tended to jam at high speeds. Designers of the now famous Qwerty layout solved this problem by creating and marketing a keyboard layout that slowed down the typist. In 1977, Mrs. Malt and Mr. Hobday began a collaboration that would result in revolutionizing the keyboard. It was based on nothing less than efficiency, accuracy, and eliminating wrist strain and injury.

Together they set out to create a keyboard that would relieve the physical stress of wrist abduction, invite strain-free movement, and take into account the varying lengths of fingers. They based the keyboard's new layout of letters, numbers and symbols on a computer analysis of letter sequence and frequency.

The resulting Maltron design is different from earlier keyboards in two major ways. First, it has a completely new shape. Second, it puts a whole new face on the keyboard letter layout.

Abduction, the outward turning of the wrists, requires sustained muscle tension, relieved, but only partly, the Maltron designers found, by slightly raising the shoulders. Abduction obviously, with time, leads to fatigue and back pain. It soon became apparent that only by splitting the keyboard could abduction be reduced.

Based on the shape of the relaxed hands, evidenced when the arms hang loosely by the side, a specific guideline for keyboard shape evolved; but since fingers are not all the same length, the heights and arcs previously evolved now needed to vary to accommodate these different finger lengths. The design is scooped. Therefore, rather than reaching out to hit its target, the finger simply aims in its direction, and, Bingo!, there it is. You can imagine what this does for speed!

After establishing the above, Mr. Hobday found, with emphasis on the split keyboard, that an opportunity had arisen to make better use of the strong and flexible thumbs, able to cover a significant area without pulling the fingers away from their "home row" positions.

In redesigning the decades-long inefficiently configured Qwerty keyboard, every opportunity was taken to redistribute work between hands and among fingers, laying out an entire new keyboard: hence, the Maltron shape.

(It is important to note, nonetheless, that those choosing to stay with their old layout can opt for either Qwerty or Dvorak layout while taking advantage of the basic brilliance of the Maltron, the Rolls Royce of the keyboard world. Trained operators staying with either Qwerty or Dvorak letter layouts can adapt to the new comfortable Maltron shape, with usually a few days — or as little as a few hours — of practice needed to regain efficiency. Learning the new layout as well may take longer, but if the time is available, it is well worth the effort, as the physical work is reduced to about one-tenth of the Qwerty value.)

The next problem was pronation, causing the hands to work horizontally across the keyboard rather than accordian style as they would surely prefer. While accordian style might be impractical in an office setting, Mr. Hobday points out that use of the concept allowed the design, expressly welcomed by operators, to alleviate the basic stress of pronation.

To give you some idea of the advanced concept of the Maltron's design, imagine that incorporated into the design — as far back as the late 1970s — is a palm resting pad in front of each finger group, allowing the palms to be lowered to the pad, for rest during pauses, without losing finger position. These palm rests promote blood flow into the hands, delaying the onset of muscle fatigue.

Finally, the Maltron keyboard boasts yet another characteristic that distinguishes it from any other keyboard I know of: Because glare of any kind can be a problem, the Maltron keyboard is made of material with a fine-grained surface that minimizes reflection.

This brings us to today, and, most probably, to the future of keyboards generally.

Is this product practical? Fair enough question. And the answer is a distinct and joyful Yes.

It is clearly established that changing from the flat to the scooped keyboard, minimizing the distance that fingers must travel, is a happy turn of events among users of the Maltron.

What is its effect on productivity? Well, users claim they attain a clear understanding of the keyboard within hours, and that within days they are up to their former speed.

Has this keyboard brought any special benefit to the office place? An intriguing result is now in and can be reported. Beyond any doubt, this keyboard is so special that it eliminates complaints of RSI/CTS in many cases. In others, it is minimizing the problem to such a surprising degree that RSI/CTS sufferers are able to hold down their current jobs, some the entire workday; others, a diminished day, yet not on the dole.

The effect of removing abduction, reducing pronation, and minimizing the distance muscles have to push a fingertip to its desired position can best be found in letters to the designers from the users. I am personally very aware of the range of reactions — from indifference to joy — that people in pain may feel toward products or services brought into the workplace. The letters penned by users of the Maltron gush from the heart with praise, relief, enthusiasm and gratefulness. I have stacks of these letters. Each of them stands alone as a monument to the Maltron.

To satisfy your curiosity, below, comparing the Qwerty, Dvorak, and the Maltron, is the Load Layout for each.

Mr. Hobday's paper, "A Keyboard to Increase Productivity and Reduce Postural Stress," as summarized above, can be obtained from him at the above address, or can be found in:

Trends in Ergonomics/Human Factors
Edited by Fereydoun Aghazadeh
Elsevier Science Publishers, BV
P. O. Box 1991
1000 BZ Amsterdam
The Netherlands

MOUSE

Bevi Chagnon
PubCom
Takoma, MD
1-301-585-8805, telephone
1-301-585-7289, fax

Under the subject heading of "mouse," I offer comments from a reader who was kind enough to call enquiring as to why I hadn't any information on the now ubiquitous "mouse."

With regard to "mice," Ms. Chagnon comments that several manufacturers have recently designed some ergonomic models that more closely fit the natural shape of the hand. Some, she says, even rotate the hand to a more natural position, with the thumb almost facing up toward the ceiling. "My clients who use mice quite a lot, such as desktop publishers, love these ergonomic mice," she notes. "They feel much more comfortable, especially after long hours at a computer."

Not having a list of these products, I renewed my contact with Ms. Chagnon, asking her if she would field calls from readers in this regard. The answer was, "happily." So, if you have questions about various mouse products available, give Ms. Chagnon a call. I hasten to add that personally, I haven't seen a one of these products, but if they are comfortable to the user, they should be investigated. Upon examination, this is the sort of product I hope you report on to your employer.

MONITOR CLEANERS

Rubbing alcohol dabbed on a piece of cotton or cloth will keep the monitor screen clean, or you can use Glass Plus. If you prefer a box of individual swabs, a box of 50 costs about $5 and can be found at most office supply stores. Clean the terminal every Monday morning and while it is cool. (If you order the special anti-glare filter from Mr. Hopper, a cleaning cloth will be enclosed with shipment of the filter. Instructions will make clear that the cloth is the *only* thing with which the filter should be cleaned.) CRT users, by the way, should usually take the trouble to clean their own terminals, rather than relying on the maintenance crew. In fact, the cleaning crew should be instructed not to touch the computer equipment. Though well-meaning, maintenance personnel often have not been instructed in the proper cleaning of the glass, and run dusty, oily, or wax cloths over the glass, making it less rather than more legible. Avoid ammonia products.

PHARMACEUTICALS

VIVA-DROPS

Vision Pharmaceuticals

1022 N. Main Street

Mitchell, SD 57301

1-800-325-6789, toll free

While he didn't recommend any specific products for ocular health, Roy Rengstorff, optometrist in Bel Air, Maryland, did send me the names of four manufacturers of vision supplements.

Products, company, and toll-free numbers are:

NUTRIVISION, Bronson 1-800-235-3200
OCUVITE, Storz/Lederle 1-800-325-9500
VIZION, Solaray 1-800-669-8877
ICAPS PLUS, La Haye Labs 1-800-344-2020

When it comes to treating eye problems nutritionally, Dr. Rengstorff has been ahead of the curve for quite some time. He also, of course, is well trained and competent in conventional treatment. But he understands that certain nutrients are associated with dry eyes, cataracts, and macular degeneration.

While there is no magic formula, simple answer, or guarantee that any nutrition program or treatment will alleviate or prevent a particular vision condition, Dr. Rengstorff feels that nutrition treatment should be considered especially in cases where present treatment has not been successful.

Having participated in or conducted extensive studies with VIVA-DROPS, a product of Vision Pharamaceuticals, Dr. Rengstorff recommends Vision's VIVA-DROPS as an effective antidote for the dry or irritated eyes that many computer workers associate with working at a monitor. While I am aware that Dr. Rengstorff is a part owner in Vision Pharmaceuticals, I also have read summaries of the results of eight different tests conducted on this product, and can report that the results are clear and stunning.

Dr. Rengstorff points out that most commercially available eye drops do not help relieve dry, irritated eyes.

He is right. In talking to thousands of computer users, finding those who had success with the typical commercial product was uncommon indeed. Yet, so many are plagued by these conditions that finding bottles of one product atop their desks was equally common.

The effectiveness of VIVA-DROPS likely lies in the quality of the product: VIVA-DROPS is a combination of anti-oxidants in an aqueous solution and contains no preservatives.

Use of this product, use of any nutrition supplement (as mentioned above), and use of any nutrition treatment, of course, should be supervised by a knowledgeable eye care professional, someone who can be expected to recognize related, overlapping, or somehow interfering conditions.

PRODUCTIVITY BREAK TIMERS

Hal Hudson

International Traders, Inc.

P. O. Box 6192

Denver, CO 80206

303-756-6985

303-758-4415, fax

As a minimum, I think full-time computer users need:

- **eye rests every five minutes;**
- **physical movement every 30 minutes;**
- **stress breaks every 60 minutes.**

So I asked Hal Hudson at International Traders in Denver to find a timer to coincide with the above schedule, to "beep":

- **every five minutes;**
- **every 30 minutes;**
- **every 60 minutes, all in different tones.**

The beeps are soft, and you can reduce volume even further by keeping the timer in your purse or desk drawer. This timer provides far more relief than its $9.95 price would suggest.

REFERENCE MATERIAL STANDS

Hal Hudson

International Traders, Inc.

P. O. Box 6192

Denver, CO 80206

1-303-756-6985, telephone

1-303-758-4415, fax

There is a big market in reference material stands, making them easy to find, with a style to meet every fancy and every need. Don't buy the least expensive copy holder without checking other models. Several basic products are available and each serves a specific job best.

•**Basic copy holder, attachable to terminal.** Made of plastic and designed to adhere to the side of the terminal. $8 to $15. Because replacing documents in this style of holder requires the use of both hands, its best use is in holding documents that do not need to be replaced often.

•Basic copy holder, free-standing. The original paper holder is the upside down V against which papers simply lean, with a ruler across the front that prevents the papers from falling off the holder. It costs $30 to $40 and works reasonably well if you leaf through stacks of invoices as your input data. If your work entails leafing through papers, avoid neckache OR an overtired arm by placing this stand about midway between desktop height and the level of the monitor.

•Updated free-standing holder. $40 to $60. Some are adjustable up and down, forward and back, and left and right. Others have a light attachment. May or may not have a bottom lip which allows for placing 10 to 20 sheets of paper.

•Motorized material stand. My favorite reference material stand is the motorized version which costs about $125. This product is worth its weight in gold. Users who also have telephone duty have reported doubling productivity.

This product looks much like the top half of a typewriter. It lights and magnifies text, and has a foot-operated scrolling mechanism which allows the operator to input information at a smooth, quick pace, improving operator efficiency and therefore productivity. For these reasons use of the copy holder lowers stress.

For a modest increase in price, you can order the adjustable arm which allows the holder to be moved to other desirable positions.

RUBBER BALLS

Small rubber balls, such as "Jacks" balls or slightly larger balls are very useful for strengthening wrists and hands, and for improving coordination. A pair of them can cost $3 to $4 dollars and can be found at a toy store.

SOFTWARE

MultiForm™

MicroNova Systems, Inc.

7597 Reynolda Station

Winston-Salem, NC 27109-7597

1-800-235-1600, toll free

1-910-922-4002, telephone

1-910-922-5204, fax

Several years ago, I was talking to someone at a computer show about how simple things can — should — be. We talked a blue streak. Lee Furr turned out to be a simplifier. We got together for a visit, and he showed me how maddening the work done by those filling out forms could be, how illogical, how confusing. And then he showed me how simple life could be for those filling out forms — short forms, long forms; narrow forms, wide; simple, or complex; single-page or multi-page forms.

MultiForm™ software reduces keystrokes for data entry on forms, minimizes errors, does math calculations, works on either pre-printed forms or prints the form itself by laser, and steamlines the hassle of otherwise filling out and printing forms.

It is, of course, extremely useful in jobs requiring the use of various type forms, and I offer you this information here because it does dances around any other electronic forms product on the market. Further, it is available only from MicroNova Systems.

EyerCise™

RAN Enterprises

One Woodland Park Drive

Haverhill, MA 01830

1-508-521-4487, telephone and fax

Because physical, visual and stress problems all overlap, it isn't possible to determine, when there are several problems, the severity of one problem if it stood alone.

Nonetheless, my surveying of computer user problems made clear that vision problems are generally the most frequent and the most severe of all computer user problems. Because our eyes are so important to us, I am always on the lookout for anything that might help computer users enhance or preserve the health of their eyes.

There's a software package on the market, EyerCise, with the purpose of helping prevent vision problems common to VDT users. While I've looked at EyerCise, because it cannot run on my machine, I haven't been able to test the product. Yet there's plenty reason to believe it is very useful. Among those recommending it are Martin Heller who reviewed the package for Windows Magazine (April 1993). Mr. Heller feels it is helping him, and he would further "recommend it to anyone who uses Windows more than four hours a day."

While allowing users to complete current tasks, EyerCise notifies them of rest breaks, scheduled either periodically or at fixed times. Each session can consist of up to four eye training exercises and nineteen stretches. Initial settings in place, a session requires only about seven minutes to complete.

To my knowledge, this is one-of-a-kind product, and I should hope large corporations especially would be aggressively looking it over. In fact, at an extremely modest $69.95, reviewing this health-software package should be very do-able on the corporate level. If you work at a large company, maybe you would just photocopy this page and slip it into the boss's IN box.

Surely EyerCise could only provide relief to the tired, red eyes and blurred vision of full time computer workers, simultaneously having a positive effect on productivity and attendance.

TELEPHONE ANSWERING ASSISTANCE EQUIPMENT

Numerous products can help people who answer telephones to keep healthy upper (cervical) vertebrae. Shoulder rests, headsets, and speaker phones are available. If you take many calls a day, visit a major telephone company and ask what can be done to prevent craning the neck while using the hands and holding the telephone. Radio Shack also has products which can help.

TIMESAVING SOFTWARE

Lee Furr

MicroNova Systems, Inc.

Drawer 7597 Reynolda Station

Winston-Salem, NC 27109-7597

One of the stress relievers I found is a type of computer software. MULTIFORM is a package for people who fill out many forms and different types of forms. MULTIFORM is a global system for forms management, requiring fewer keystrokes per entry, minimizing errors, making math calculations when necessary, and in general streamlining the form-filling application process. It is extremely useful in tasks requiring the filling out of preprinted forms.

WRIST RESTS

Jack C. Hicks

Ergonomic Design Specialties

10687 Northglenn Drive

Northglenn, CO 80233

1-303-452-8331, telephone

Wrist rests can be custom-made to fit into the space in front of the keyboard, and they can be reasonably priced. Sharon

Danaan at 9 to 5, the National Association for Working Women, reports they are quite pleased with wrist rests they got from Ergonomic Design Specialties.

CRT-User Periodicals

Jim Kinsella
CTDNews
Center for Workplace Health
P. O. Box 239
Haverford, PA 19041
1-800-554-4283, toll free
1-215-896-2770, telephone
1-215-896-1488, fax

Everybody needs to know about and will, I hope, take a look at at least one edition of *CTDNews.*

Statistics? Do you want to know what all the various kinds of repetitive strain injury (RSI) and cumulative trauma disorders (CTD) are costing you? Can you afford not to know how RSI and other CTD can be remedied? Prevented?

Call *CTDNews.* Their purpose is keeping you up to the minute in information that makes for a healthier workplace and that can save you money.

As you consider that thirty cents of your every worker's compensation dollar is being spent on RSI and CTD, consider the list of publications they've developed for you:

**CTDNews,* a monthly, reports on legal and regulatory issues, including lawsuits, OSHA enforcement and pending legislation. It comes with two special reports. In 1993, they included a report aimed at helping the individual sufferer and a report listing preventive products. (You can pick up all twelve issues of Volume 1 (1991) for $85, and Volume 2 (1992) for $95. This includes the two special reports.)

**CTD Legal Guide,* a 350-page tome put together with the help of seven attorneys specializing in RSI. It covers such subjects as product liability, workers' compensation, and the American Disabilities Act, and is priced at a very reasonable $125.

*There's the *Prevention Handbook,* $45, which includes the pull-out graphics from each of the year's twelve monthly issues, 23 graphics in all.

*Be on the lookout for *Ergonomics Guide,* now in its last phase of completion. It will feature fully 1000 products that show promise for alleviating RSI.

Consider their other services: As the Center is basically an occupational health research company, they do on-call research for large corporations and also on an individual basis.

Wondering if they can help you? The Center's staff includes ergonomists, and physical and occupational therapists, as well as professional researchers.

The Center for Workplace Health Information is a wholly independent occupational health research company. *CTDNews* itself is recommended reading by NIOSH, OSHA, leading researchers and corporate safety directors throughout North America. For more information, call their toll free number, 1-800-554-4283.

DPMA Newsletter
505 Busse Highway
Park Ridge, IL 60068
1-708-825-8124, telephone

Data Processing Management Association offers a quarterly publication. This organization aims to develop better managers, and their two publications frequently have information that helps managers deal with stress and other health issues confronting the CRT user.

Because DPMA serves the interest of managers, supervisors

might request company help in funding a subscription. Their information is useful.

Data Entry Management Association
101 Merrit 7, Corporate Park, 5th Floor
Norwalk, CT 06851
1-203-846-3777, telephone

Data Entry Management Association's monthly newsletter. focuses on managerial issues. The subscription rate varies as they publish four different newsletters. Give your supervisor a subscription for Christmas. Help your supervisor help you.

VDT News
P.O. Box 1799, Grand Central Station
New York, NY 10163
1-212-517-2802, telephone

One of the industry flagstaffs is *VDT News,* the VDT health and safety report, which appears bimonthly and costs $87/year. They report on industry standards, guidelines, research, and all the latest news, including conferences on VDT ergonomics.

9 to 5
National Association of Working Women
614 Superior Avenue, NW #852
Cleveland, OH 44113-1306
1-216-566-9308, telephone

The National Association of Working Women, better known as 9 to 5, does everything it can for computer operators.

Full-time CRT operators should seriously consider joining, if they do not already. The Association's annual fee, based on your annual salary, breaks down to about a nickel a day. It goes toward representing you in Washington, D.C., before Congress, and before other interested parties. 9 to 5's Job Problem Hotline (800-522-0925) is a national job counseling service. Call and get free advice on your job problems.

Members also receive excellent publications, including "Improving Office Air Quality" ($1.50, and I advise everyone to order it), "Career Options" ($15), and "Legal Rights" ($4). I love the 9 to 5 Survival Kit, a tote bag filled with a Superwoman note pad, the Office Worker Survival Guide, Pepto Bismol, and the 9 to 5 whistle reminding you that you can call for help. The bag is a good size for carrying lunch, a book, and a small radio. The whole package is only $7 to members ($10 to non-members).

***Vitality* Magazine**
Vitality, Inc.
8080 North Central, LB 78
Dallas, TX 75206-1818
1-800-299-8680, toll free
214-691-1480, telephone
214-891-8202, fax

Here is a magazine for those of you who want a lot of information squeezed into short sentences, and stories squeezed into but a few paragraphs. It is imposible to allocate the typical amount of space to this publication and tell you all it contains. (Your best bet is to call and ask for a sample copy.)

Nonetheless, suffice it to say that monthly, this little 30-page magazine brings you a festival of good ideas, and is laden with positive actions you can take, all stated in brevity. The layout is light and easy to read.

There are very good stress relievers, excellent environmental tips (things that help the universe and your wallet). There are doable diets, simple recipes, safety quizzes that are fun while educating, reasonable tips on exercise and exercises. What few products are advertised seem useful and affordable

The annual subscription rate is a reasonable $12.99, about half of which they earmark for postage. In terms of your health and well-being, if you'll heed their words, you'll get your annual fee returned to you every month.

Vitality, Inc., puts out several other publications. For instance, the October 1993, 16 pages, was a special entitled Corporate Outreach Issue. It's a bit pricy at $120 annually. But if you're in management, you should find it useful. And it comes ready to file, with three holes punched into the side.

WOHRC Newsletter
Women's Occupational Health Resource Center
117 St. John's Place
Brooklyn, NY 11217
1-718-230-8822, telephone

Dr. Jeanne Stellman, formerly with Columbia University, publishes an excellent newsletter on women and the workplace in general, and almost always offers something new on computer workstations. Its annual cost is $15 for individuals and $25 for institutions. The protection it provides your health is worth many times the cost of the annual subscription rate. Ask a friend to subscribe with you. That would be only $7.50 apiece for the entire year. It is highly recommended to anyone who cares about the effect of certain work practices, new findings in research, and new legislation regarding the computer workplace. Its bias only adds to its professionalism and objectivity.

CRT-User Books

Ahuja, Savitri, *Savitri's Way to Perfect Fitness through Hatha Yoga.* New York: Simon & Schuster, 1979.

For 15 years, I experienced considerable back pain resulting from two car accidents. Then a cousin suggested I join her at her evening yoga instruction. It was there I met the remarkable Savitri Ahuja, instructor nonpareil. In spite of the fact I was usually in above average physical condition, under Ms. Ahuja's tutelage I was soon in extraordinary physical condition, knowing not even a hint of back trouble. My posture improved, my breathing changed — forever — and my blood pressure almost disappeared.

Once a week I attended a hour's instruction, and on each of the other six days of the week, I faithfully executed very simple stretching exercises for 20 minutes every morning and 10 minutes every evening.

For you self starters who enjoy doing things for yourself that have a positive, lifelong effect, you'll be happy to know that Ms. Ahuja put it all in print. Your can write her direct for a copy of her lovely publication on yoga ($12.95, no shipping charge).

To obtain copies, write Savrita Ahuja at 5180 34th Street, NW, Washington, DC 20016.

Cohen, Barbara G. F., "Organizational Factors Affecting Stress in the Clerical Worker," in *Human Aspects in Office Automation,* edited by Barbara G. F. Cohen. Amsterdam: Elsevier Science Publishers.

In a very well written document, Ms. Cohen starts with how organizations can enhance worker self-esteem through encouraging work satisfaction, then points out that most of one's "waking hours are spent doing or thinking" about his job, and (therefore) that "the most salient factor found for living a long life was whether or not a person liked his job." She moves quickly on to the significance of status and what it means in terms of how we are treated by others — hence, how we perceive ourselves. Clearly, as she points out, self perception "is not a trivial matter."

Ms. Cohen continues: Lower-status occupations are associated with increased levels of heart disease and with poorer mental health, "particularly evident where work was repetitive, or involved only slight amounts of physical activity."

This is a paper that I hope will reach all management. Its telling is so simple, its conclusions so obvious.

This report does not portray a writer who is over-sympathetic. It is factual and to the point. Cohen zeroes in on the experiences of full-time VDT users, isolating the working conditions that can lead to trouble: Repetitive work, lack of control, insufficient physical activity, high stress, low pay, boredom, lack of challenge, lack of chance to get ahead, lack of direct involvement with organizational goals.

Ms. Cohen addresses, in simple terms, the importance of openly sharing information that affects the organization as a whole, the importance of participating in decision making, how job automation can limit skills and expectations. Consider her point: "One might surmise that the wonderful ability of the new word processor units (this was 1981!) to make changes so easily would increase productivity. Unfortunately, too often what is increased is the number of changes. It is not atypical for one clerical person to type for 10 or more staff members. When each of those staff members believes it is 'no trouble' to change a word or a paragraph, after receiving the letter-perfect copy, more and more changes are requested. Thus, a great deal of extra work is generated. A lot of extra time is spent, but what are the results? Instead of more reports getting out, the same report gets out more times. Multiply this 10 times or more and the clerical worker feels frustrated and yet has no outlet for justifiable anger."

Obviously, having responsibility but no control over any situation can cause enormous stress.

Consider Ms. Cohen's observation: "An overload in a computer aborts the program." Take it from there.

There is so much of value in this report. But just one last example. Consider the computer user who is given work at the last minute, with an unfair deadline for completing the job. The boss, who submitted the material late, still can say (and how many times have you heard this one), "I gave it to Rachel, but she still has it." Through greater effort, working her fingers to the bone, Rachel makes the deadline. Praise? Reward? Bonus? Raise? Promotion?

Poignantly, Ms. Cohen points out, the next time around the supervisor says, "Take it to Rachel, she always gets it done."

These are the exasperations of the airline reservationist, the accounting assistant in the computerized division of a huge company, the booking clerk for a major hotel chain, the check-out person at the grocery store, and, nowadays, countless others, literally tens of millions of others.

How can we improve work and thus life for these people who are the backbone of America while getting the work done efficiently? Start with the basic premise offered in this paper, understand the humanizing elements that raise self-esteem and thereby enhance well-being, and raise the output of all employees.

Last, Ms. Cohen points out that it is the system that creates most clerical and secretarial worker problems, and it is the system that can eliminate these problems. She also provides more than adequate fodder for those running the system to come up with ideas for changing it,

Finding these simple, clear, logical papers is as difficult as it is a joy. Thus, in my enthusiasm over this paper, I set out on a mission to find Ms. Cohen. For those of you who might want to know, she is now at the national office of the Internal Revenue Service in Washingotn, D. C., having a rewarding time in their Office of Human Resource Modernization.

Donkin, Scott W., *Sitting on the Job.* New York: Houghton, Miflin, 1991.

Scott Donkin, a chiropractor, has written a definitive layman's guide for the worker who sits all day at a desk. Although there is some overlap with my book, you will find a different presentation with additional useful information, all in very readable form.

Dul, J. and Weerdmeester, B., *Ergonomics for Beginners, A Quick Reference Guide.* London: Taylor and Francis, 1993.

Because I couldn't put it better than their own literature stated, I quote Taylor and Francis on this valuable publication:

> This book, a new, fully revised and updated edition of the Dutch classic *Vademecum Ergonomie,* offers an excellent practical introduction for anyone who feels ergonomics can bring benefits to people and the perfomance of tasks in work and domestic environments. . . . Embracing the concepts of design tasks and the environment for human comfort and satisfaction as well as for optimum perfomance, the book shows, in an accessible and easily understandable fashion, the steps by which managers, workers, and users can achieve an appropriate balance.

In the light of recent and forthcoming legislation, and the growing public interest in and awareness of ergonomics and human factors, this book is essential, and an invaluable addition to anyone's bookshelf at work or at home.

Can you afford not to read it?

My response, in a word, is No. Anyone seriously involved in ergonomics should have this handy reference book whose clean, clear, simple layout and concise approach to the topic makes it eminently useful and readable.

First published in 1963, the book in its 1991 edition (entirely revised) is already into its second printing in 1993 alone, no doubt because it allows readers to easily grasp the major elements of ergonomics with the simplicity that should and can be possible.

Ellis, John Marion, M.D., *Free of Pain.* Linden, Texas: Natural Food Associates, 1989.

Included among the various subjects covered in Dr. Ellis's book is Repetitive Strain Injury (RSI). Of special interest is his coverage of carpal tunnel syndrome.

Obtain this book by writing to Natural Food Associates, P.O. 210, Atlanta, Texas, 75551 or call 1-903-796-3612.

Juliussen, Karen, and Juliussen, Egil, Ph.D., *The 1993 Computer Industry Almanac.* Incline Village, Nevada: Computer Industry Almanac, Inc., 1993.

If you want to know virtually everything in the world going on about any aspect of the computer world, this is your opportunity.

The 1993 *Almanac* lists anything you ever wanted to know about companies, magazines, newsletters, research companies, associations, organizations, user groups, book publishers, testing companies, conferences, peoples — the list goes on.

That isn't why I list the book, however. The Juliussens have proved the computer can ingest everything there is to ingest, and throw it our in an orderly and useful fashion, but for my purposes, I am rather jumping the gun in recommending the 1993 edition. While it contains a modest amount of ergonomics related information, future editions — probably in their 1994 edition— will contain a host of information about ergonomics, ergonomically designed products, ergonomic conferences, ergonomic publications, and so on.

Having spoken with the Egil Juliussen about their revisions, I was concerned that my update might not keep pace with their update, and you, the reader would lose out re good ergonomic related information.

As management desperately needs current and relevant information, I wanted to get ahead of the curve and tell you of what is being prepared for you.

By the way, as with future editions, this massive document (800 pages) is available on disk. For those looking for *the* authoritative — complete and exhaustive — source of ergonomic information, the Juliussens are getting it ready for you in their next edition. Be on the look-out.

Contact Computer Industry Almanac, Inc., at 225 Allen Way, Incline Village, Lake Tahoe, NV, 89451-9308. Telephone 1-800-377-6810 toll free, or 1-702-831-2288 (Pacific time). Fax to 1-702-831-8610, or send E Mail to 491-9887, MCI.

Report, Essi Systems, Inc., 70 Otis Street , San Francisco, CA 94103 (1-800-252-ESSI, telephone; 1-415-252-8224, telephone 1-415-252-5732, fax)

Because my book is written for computer users and not especially for managers, time and again I urge you to get things under control, to take charge of your life, to make things happen *for* you, not *to* you. However, since I hope that many managers are also going to read my book, I wanted to take the time to say what everyone knows: It obviously matters whether or not people work in dysfunctional systems; setting priorities, using time efficiently, devising procedures, designing jobs, are but a few items critical to how people react to stress within any system.

One day, someone landed a report on my desk, "Why Stress Programs Don't Work," a three-part series by Esther M. Orioli, CEO of Essi Systems. I found it sensible good reading. Although I don't know Essi firsthand and so cannot actually recommend their work, the additional written information I requested and received from them was equally informative and interesting.

Essi apparently understands that different groups of employees experience and cope differently with stress, and that therefore stress programs should not assume a homogeneity in their target audiences. Particularly, I was delighted to find that research conducted by Ms. Orioli over a six-year period which involved 1,500 people at 40 companies. Men and women reacted very differently to stress in this study; the highest stress was found among the lowest levels of the organization. These two observations interest me because I believe they will prove to be among the three most critical aspects as to who gets Repetitive Strain Injury (with the third, while most important, is being previous injury to the spine, as shown in the Appendix, by Dr. Dickson).

Based on their reading matter, Essi should be able to provide you information that helps you see how your organization can use stress in positive ways. Information based on their sizeable database (built on results with 2000 companies), should be able to help you predict hot spots of dysfunction.

Faber, William J., D.O. and Walker, Morton, D.P. M. ***Pain, Pain Go Away.*** **San Jose, California: Ishi Press, International, 1990.**

Being firmly in the self-help camp, I found this book very interesting. The authors make a heroic effort to educate consumer-laymen, victimized by and weary from the expense and ineffectiveness of conventional treatment and drugs, to say nothing of chronic joint pain. Whereas numerous books address individual joint problems, *Pain, Pain, Go Away* is devoted specifically to the cause and correction of dysfunction arising from unstable joints, instability arising from "degenerative disease, overly lax ligaments, torn tendons, ruptured discs, and crushed cartilage." Considering, like most, surgery to be a very serious matter, I was pleased to find the chapter on Carpal Tunnel Syndrome telling how "reconstructive therapy" can function as a stand-alone alternative to CTS surgery.

The therapy may not work for everyone, but anyone due for CTS surgery should read this book, available in the U.S. from Ishi Press International, 76 Bonaventura Drive, San Jose, CA 95134 and in Europe from Ishi Press International, 20 Bruges Place, London NW1 OTE, UK.

Loss, Martha, ***At Least Every Twenty Minutes.*** **Newton, Massachusetts: Oakfield Associates, 1993.**

For a decade, Martha Loss has been helping organizations and people with the ergonomic challenges of intensive computerized work such as repetitive strain injuries. The hallmark of Ms. Loss' innovative approach is her unique perspective of the role of training and the latest information for managers and computer users.

While adjustments to equipment and furniture to fit the

physical needs of the individual and the demands of the job are important, Ms. Loss believes that training in computer wellness and injury prevention techniques are critical to everyone who uses a computer and wants to stay healthy.

Her new book, due out soon, is both entertaining and informative. She discusses the ergonomic factors (equipment, furniture, and job tasks) and the human factors (work habits, physical and psychological aspects, general wellness awareness) that combine to enhance the human-computer relationship.

Although I haven't been in a classroom where she was teaching, a former Harvard Business School colleague intimately aware of her style promises that Ms. Loss offers useful and effectiv information with a sense of humor to teach exercises, work habits, and overall wellness tips that can improve your computer work and play experience and reduce injuries. Her interactive workbook, says her colleague, has been very successful for both employers and employees

For information regarding the full range of management and ergonomic services that Ms. Loss offers, give her a call. I can tell you this: You'll not only find her knowledgeable, you'll really enjoy talking to her.

Morehouse, Laurence E. and Gross, Leonard, *Total Fitness in 30 Minutes a Week.* New York: Packet Books, a division of Simon & Schuster.

Most of us feel there isn't enough time in the day to meet our commitments as it is. So, where in the schedule do we weasel in exercise, something we don't want to do in any event?

Morehouse and Gross set out to prove that "a desirable level of fitness can be achieved without sweat and strain." Their effort shows how to slow the aging process, debunks numerous physical fitness myths, addresses maximizing nutrition, tells you how to make a fitness period of your shower, and on and on.

You'll be amazed by the amount of information in this fast, easy book, and you'll be delighted to know how simple being fit can be.

Various publications of the the Arbets Miljo Institute

Since the early 1970s, Jorgen Winkel has addressed the effect of sitting for long periods of time. In "On the Significance of Physical Activity in Sedentary Work", Dr. Winkel states that "the ergonomic advantages of improved design of seated work-stations may partly be eliminated by the increased time spent in the same position." He emphasizes that some stresses and strains are good, and suggests, "the aim of ergonomic interventions should therefore be to optimize rather than reduce physical stress as far as possible. This may be attained by organizational changes in working routines rather than constructional improvements in the workstations." Indeed, some companies have the finest furniture available and still have worker discomfort. Organizational changes in work routines, an important aspect of ergonomics, are now being researched thoroughly.

Dr. Winkel is happy to share any of his information with you, including any of his numerous other publications.

To obtain the latest publications, write Professor Jorgen Winkel, Arbets Miljo Institute, National Institute of Occupational Health, Division of Applied Work Physiology, 171 84 Solna, Sweden.

Various publications from Fixtures Furniture

By request, Fixtures Furniture will send you any of several publications by qualified professionals.

Enlightening information on seating is presented in "Balanced Seating," by Dr. A. C. Mandal, chief surgeon of the Finsen Institute in Copenhagen, Denmark. Dr. Mandal explains the logic and addresses the comfort of assuming a seated position essentially the same as that found in horseback riding.

Another paper available from Fixtures Furniture is entitled "The Ergonomics of VDT Seating," by Marvin Dainoff, a consultant to NIOSH and director of the Center of Ergonomic Research at the University of Miami at Oxford, Ohio. Dr. Dainoff has also conducted extensive research on CRT user problems and remedies.

To obtain publications, write Fixtures Furniture, P.O. Box 6346, Kansas City, Missouri 64126-2825. Telephone 816-241-4500.

CONSULTANTS

Richard E. Barry
Consultant
3808 No. Albemarle Street
Arlington, VA 22207
1-703-241-3808 telephone
1-703-241-7968 fax

You will have noticed, prior to now, that my book hasn't once mentioned radiation as connected with the use of computer equipment nor has it mentioned electromagnetic fields (EMF). Neither of these subjects is within my expertise, and to hold out my opinion for examination would be naive at best. Nonetheless, I feel strongly that this is a subject not being examined with any prudence in this country. For more than one reason — as noted in the acknowledgements — I am grateful to have met Rick Barry.

If I cannot hold out my opinion regarding the potential hazards of working too close to computer and other office equipment, I can at least introduce you to someone who steers the course of what he calls "prudent avoidance."

Keeping somewhat apprised of environmental matters, and having read Paul Brodeur's book *Currents of Death,* highly recommended reading, I became alarmed by information on extra-low frequency EMFs, what are called ELFs, and therefore very interested in and impressed by Mr. Barry's work in EMF radiation mitigation planning.

I met Mr. Barry at the World Bank where he was Chief Officer, Human Factors, Technology and Facilities Integration. There, he led groundbreaking projects in facilities management in construction disturbance mitigation planning, aimed at minimizing the impact of demolition and new construction on adjoining buildings where continuing operations were being carried out during construction. His purpose at the World Bank has been to implement the "prudent avoidance" policy and approach to EMF mitigation in new office building construction. His work has employed specific strategies for reducing EMFs from building service systems and office equipment. A number of very cost-effective measures were included in the construction of the new World Bank building in downtown Washington, DC.

As reported in the March 1993 issue of Bank's World:

* The building's main electrical switching equipment was moved from where the service comes in under the sidewalks to the fifth basement parking level, thus distancing the equipment from areas where staff may be sitting all day.

* The smaller electrical switching equipment on each floor was mounted in electrical rooms on the walls facing the elevator lobbies rather than on the rear walls abutting typical office areas.

* Electrical rooms on each floor were kept somewhat larger than the minimum essential size for normal maintenance to provide greater distance between the floor switching equipment and the office spaces.

* Fluorescent lights use electronic rather than electromagnetic ballast to transform incoming power to operate the light bulbs. This not only has a low EMF profile, but, according to a British study, reduces headache and eyestrain. Additionally, a multi-light ballast was used so that one ballast serves more than one light fixture, thus reducing cost, energy consumption and EMF emissions.

Numerous other measures were developed, but this gives those of you becoming familiar with the area of human factors something to think about. Given the strict measures being taken by some countries, I would urge you to read further the accounts as reported in *Microwave News,* March 1993; in *VDT News* in May/June1993; and in *PC World,* in the column "Real Problems, Real Solutions," September 1993.

If you're considering renovation of a current structure or building a new structure, I'd urge you to contact Mr. Barry for consultation and guidance.

Mr. Barry is a a consultant who has worked in cross-disciplinary fields with a number of clients internationally, including the Inter-American Development Bank, the International Federation of Red Cross and Red Crescent Societies, the U.S. National Archives and Records Administration, the World Bank, and the UN Advisory committee for Co-ordination of Information Systems.

Penny Edwards
Nutrition Consultant
2370 Hidalgo Avenue
Los Angeles, CA 90039
1-213-662-0783, telephone
1-213-644-1410, fax

It was approximately 14 years ago that I first talked to Penny Edwards on the matter of nutrition and its critical role in health and the workplace, given our now overprocessed food, stripped of original nourishment, and the omnipresent candy machine.

Today I am still amazed by the wealth of knowledge this one person has on nutrition — and I myself own some 200 well-heeled health and nutrition books.

Several years ago, and because of the extraordinary vision problems I found among full-time monitor users, I called to ask what, if any, specific supplements were essential to ocular health generally, and especially to the ocular health of full-time monitor users.

Ms. Edwards explained the role of vitamin C in vision, pointing out that, along with the adrenal and pituitary glands, the lens of the eye contains the greatest concentration of vitamin C found anywhere in the body! (She graciously thanked Linus Pauling, Nobel science winner for this nugget.)

Ms. Edwards now consults on her own. Included in her expertise are proper vitamin mixes not only for ocular health, but for such occupational hazards as Carpal Tunnel Syndrome and other Repetitive Strain Injuries.

Any company wanting to investigate its absenteeism and to improve its attendance record would be well advised to call in Ms. Edwards.

Appendix

The Carpal Tunnel/Double Crush Syndromes Institute, Inc.

2909 Reynolda Road

Winston-Salem, NC 27106

1-919-777-8450, telephone

1-919-777-8435, fax

Chiropractic Management, under Workers' Compensation Board Criteria, of Carpal Tunnel/Double Crush Syndromes: A Thirteen-Case Retrospective Analysis.

By Thomas A. Dickson, DC, CN, President of The Carpal Tunnel/Double Crush Syndromes Institute, and Clinical Director of the Dickson Clinic of Chiropractic, Winston-Salem, NC

Patient Origin

An initial retrospective analysis was performed between January 1992 and August 1993. Examination of 13 Workers' Compensation Board Patients, 77% of whom were previously diagnosed by either orthopedic surgeons or neurologists, were diagnosed and treated by The Carpal Tunnel/Double Crush Syndromes Institute (CDSI) procedures. The patients were referred from three companies; one predominantly in the textile industry with employees engaged in small motor skills activity; the other two with employees engaged heavily in computer workstation skills activity.

Chiropractic History in Double Crush Syndrome

Since Upton and McComas (1) first reported the existence of the Double Crush Syndrome in 1973, interest in the chiropractic community has been to determine chiropractic's clinical place in the growing diagnosis of Carpal Tunnel Syndrome and Double Crush Syndrome. Cramer and Cramer (2) and Mariano, et. al. (3), have presented convincing articles on interprofessional treatment, combining the known effectiveness of manual manipulation, as reported by Loes, et. al. (4), with the diagnostic abilities of both the medical and chiropractic professions.

Cervical Trauma

In this CDSI retrospective analysis, 69% of the cases had experienced previous cervical spine trauma, all in the form of a car accident. From the point of trauma to the point of examination ranged from three months to 28 years, with an average of 12.6 years. The average time reported from the origin of any arm or hand symptoms was 2.5 years. Thus, an average 10-year time frame existed for these patients, for the development of the distal symptom from the proximal trauma.

Axon Compression

Citing Nemoto, et. al. (5), this proximal compression will block the distribution of nutrients to the distal nerve axon, making it more susceptible to injury. Thus, in all 13 cases where wrist symptoms were reported, along with various peripheral nerve conduction velocity (PNCV) and electromyograph (EMG) readings, it is conceivable that the axon damage through nutrient deficiency was variable and thus response to treatment would follow: The patient would improve.

Treatment Protocol

Treatment included activator chiropractic spinal adjustments, soft wrap wrist supports, B-complex vitamin support, adjustments to the radius and carpal bones, adjustments to the computer workstation that minimized neck muscle tension, and neck and shoulder muscle strengthening exercises. When possible, ice therapy was applied at the patient's workplace. This concept of in-plant treatment, while the patient remained at work, allowed for greater control of the protocol while eliminating possible high risk activities that prolonged periods at home might present.

The Dominant Hand

Fifty percent of the cases were right-handed, with 30% left-handed and 20% bilateral involvement. Of these, there was a 99% dominant-handed involvement, with hand initial symptoms. The second hand, when it became symptomatic, did so an average of 17 months later. One hundred percent of the post-surgical cases treated were in the dominant hand.

Time Lost from Work

Modified duty or alternative workstations were used in all the cases. The patient with computer-based jobs were asked to alter their workstations to comply with eye screen distance and height according to findings of Lacey, et. al. (6). The use of telephones was altered to use of a headset, to avoid the constant lateral hyperflexion of the neck associated with trying to do telephone, monitor, and keyboard work simultaneously.

Computer Operator Syndrome

One computer operator with dominant arm and hand pain suffered a significant cervical spine trauma 28 years previous to examination at CDSI. She was assigned work at a computer workstation and within one year began to report symptoms of TSI. Examination found median nerve parasthesias, along with C6 hyperextension subluxation disc syndrome, along with a loss of cervical lordosis. The workstation was evaluated onsite, as per research by Lacey and Dickson (6). Several changes were made, including screen height and arm placement. Once out of pain and gaining strength, the patient was reassigned to computer work but on a reduced time period of four hours a day. Within two days, the patient reported a gradual return of forearm aching. She was stopped from doing further computer work and assigned light duty work. The symptoms abated within one week. She was subsequently returned to her computer work, and once agian symptoms returned to the forearm. It became apparent that the degree of cervical instability at the C6/C7 level caused to the forearm and hand symptoms to return every time the patient was reassigned computer work. This return of symptoms recurred three different times, finally ending up with the patient permanently changing jobs. At the patient's four-month check, she happily reports minimal symptoms.

Three Cases Post-Treatment: Special Circumstances

In two cases, the number of repetitive hand and forearm movements approached 3,000 per eight-hour shift. These two females placed mailings in a folder and used a labeler. During treatment by CDSI, they were intitially placed in physically less strenuous jobs. As symptoms abated, they were gradually returned, as a test, to half days and then to full days at their former work. In these cases, within a two-week period, shoulder and forearm symptoms reappeared gradually and then increased. It became evident that the permanent nature of the cervical degeneration found in both cases could not withstnad the high degree of trauma. One of these patients has since received a Carpal Tunnel Release (CTR) in the dominant hand, and the second has subsequently been examined by several medical doctors, with no definitive or conclusivne action taken to date.

The third patient, in the textile industry, was in a hgihly repetitive folding job. The patient's initial neck and arm symptoms were reduced following the standard CDSI treatment protocol, and she was returned to work. The level of pain at the time of release was minimal, and the patient desired to return to work at her regular position. The patient's treatment was terminated. She subsequently requested and received an operation on the dominant arm elbow, for ulnar nerve entrapment. This decision was solely the patient's and was done under the individual's health insurance, as it was not approved by the employer's Workers' Compensation Board insurance. Evaluation since surgery has seen an increase in the pain level of the operated arm and a loss of mobility in the elbow joint. At the present time, she is working in increased pain, with no further treatment available.

The high-risk employee, as determined by this retrospective, would be the 38-year-old right-handed female with a previoulsy untreated cervical spine trauman of 12 years duration. Placing this patient on an intensive, repetitive, small motor skills job proves to be a high risk endeavor.

Conclusion

This CSI retrospective found that within the WCB setting, the average cost per completed diagnosis of Double Crush Syndrome was $1,347, including the cost of x-rays, examination and chiropractic treatment. The average number of treatments ranged from 20 to 42, with an average treatment time of 3.3 months.

If chiropractic is to continue being competitive in the health care arena (7), it must develop ways of providing the patient with pre-surgical choices for the range of conditions with similar medical diagnoses.

The 1993 Manga report on Ontario Chiropractic (8), along with the report by Stano, et. al. (9), clearly identifies the growing acceptance of chiropractic care. This inclusion either in the Health Maintenance Organization (HMO/Preferred Provider

Organization (PPO) [HMO/PPO] setting (10), or in fee for service, has flourished.

The future of CDSI research in the field of cumulative trauma will be to continue to produce interprofessional outcomes studies on cumulative trauma disorders of the neck, shoulder, arm, and wrist. This will be accomplished through the development of greater cooperation, as suggested by Curtis (11), with primary contact family practitioners and the chiropractic profession. Currently, CDSI is establishing protocol iwht neurologists for pre- and post-PNCV/EMG testing, to blend in with a strict CSI protocol in the chiropractic setting. It is the author's hope that such clinical research will only enhance the patient's chance of recovery from these ever-increasing soft tissue disorders.

1. Upton, A., McComas, A.J. "The Double Crush in Nerve Entrapment Syndromes." *Lancet,* 1973; 2:359.

2. Cramer, S.R., Cramer, L.M. "Double Crush Syndrome: A Chiropractic/Surgical Approach to Treatment," *Digest of Chiropractic Economics,* 1991; 2:14.

3. Marinao, K.A., McDougle, M.A., Tanksley, G.W. "Double Crush Syndrome: Chiropractic Care on an Entrapment Neuropathy, *Journal of Manipulative and Physiological Therapeutics,* 1991; 4:262.

4. Koes, B. W., Couter, L.W., van Maneren, J., et. al., "The Effectiveness of Manual Therapy, Physiotherapy, and Treatment by the General Practitioner for Nonspecific Back and Neck Complaints, *Spine,* 1992; 1:28.

5. Nemoto, K., Matsumoto, N., Tazaki, K., et. al., "An experimental Study of the 'Double Crush' Hypothesis," *Journal of Hand Surgery,* 1987; 4:552.

6. Lacy, J.S., Dickson, T.A., Levenson, H.A., *How to Survive Your Computer Workstation,* CRT Services, 1990.

7. Stano, M., "A Comparison of Health Care Costs for Chiropractic and Medical Patients," *Journal of Manipulative and Physiological*

Therapeutics, 1993; 5:1.

8. Manga, P., Angus, D., Papdopoulos, C., Swan, W., *The Effectiveness and Cost-effectiveness of Chiropractic Management of Low-back Pain,* Ontario Ministry of Health, 1993.

9. Stano, M., Ehrhart, J., Allenburg, T.J., "The Growing Role of Chropractic in Health Care Delivery," *Journal of American Health Policy,* 1992; 6:39.

10. Dickson, T.A., "The Initial Statistics from Chiropractic Managed Care Panel Acting as a PP Under an HMS," Dickson Chiropractic, 1993.

11. Curtis, P., Bove, G., "Family Physicians, Chiropractors, and Back Pain," *Journal of Family Practice,* 1992. 5:551.

Index

Mark Twain once observed that there is nothing so uncommon in this world as "common sense." In this book, Ms. Lacey belies that aphorism by bringing that rare attribute to bear on an area of our lives and activities which needs some common sense. As we spend increasing numbers of hours at computer workstations, both in homes and workplaces, this wise, concise, practical work will be increasingly valuable. I recommend it to anyone who is concerned with such matters.

Donald M. Hayes, M.D., and Medical Director
Sara Lee Corporation

I found the book accessible, excellent, and entertaining, and...wish you every success with this interesting project.

Richard Steele, Publisher
Taylor & Francis Ltd.
London, England

Your book is a valuable guide and tool for the millions of VDT users in industry and commerce, and I predict it will be widely used inasmuch as there are no other manuals or books which equal its coverage and detail. I am sure there must be millions of VDT operators with vision problems who will find help with your book...Push ahead with your efforts, for they are especially valuable to the common sufferer at the VDT workstation. Your warning should be: Don't wait till your eyes go bad in work, for then it will be too late to take the precautions necessary to making the workstation benign. Good luck!

Karl U. Smith, Ph.D., Professor Emeritus
Department of Psychology
University of Wisconsin

We just received the galleys for your book—it looks terrific, a real aid to the millions of people working on VDTs. We're all looking forward to its publication. Here's to a successful launch.

Karen Nussbaum, former Executive Director
9 to 5, National Association of Working Women

Just had a call from someone at the American Optometric Association...who was very complimentary about the book, and felt it filled a void in the information for CRT users. Well, you can imagine my delight!

Howard A. Levenson, Optometrist and co-author
Optometrist of the Year, California 1991

Madelyn Jennings shared your book with me, and I wanted you to kow that I consider it one of the best I've seen on this topic. As Gannett's training director and chair of our CTD task force, I've examined a wide variety of information resources. Yours is excellent—readable, practical, and comprehensive...and will be an excellent supplemental resource. Thanks for thinking of us.

Chris Landauer, Director, Training & Development
Gannett

It isn't often that a book on computers, or more specifically, working with computers, can be classified as entertaining, but this one is. It offers a refreshingly personal approach and yet at the same time it has much worthwhile to say...Two niggles: I found the diagrams a bit too simple, and wished there were an index. But, all in all, very well-thought-out, easy to read, and full of common sense.

Anne Grimshaw, Editor
Information Management and Technology
London, England

Ms. Lacey has written a self-help book for anyone who uses computers—supervisors, technical systems people, corporate executives, and probably most important, the ordinary but necessary people whose office work is greatly involved with computer workstation interaction. People who design computer workstations, particularly those who test them in the final stages, should read the book and think about what it is telling them. Ms. Lacey makes many interesting suggestions that workers could try in order to improve their jobs and work environments. The results could be a big payoff to the individuals, as well as the companies and institutions that employ them.

J. Fendrich
Computing Reviews
Association for Computing Machinery

I am writing you a few lines to tell you how much I appreciated your book received earlier this fall. I read it while traveling over the Atlantic to U.S., and I think the book is very useful to people who have to work much with the screen every day. I am going to inform my colleagues about your book. Thank you for the book!

Nils Sovik, Professor of Education
Universitetet i Trondheim
Dragvoll, Norway

Congratulations on your book. It explains what must be done for office workers, and at the same time explains proper use of vitamin B6. Call if you would like me to provide a quote for the cover of your book. I am happy to do so.

John Marion Ellis, M.D.
Mt. Pleasant, Texas

Feedback from one of our managers: He hailed the "down to earth, how-to" tone of the book, saying that its practicality made it a valuable handbook for CRT users. He particularly praised the section on minimizing eyestrain. Playing devil's advocate, he wondered if some managers might view the book with an eye to potential triggering of "stress related" injury suits by employees. However, it seems to be that the book makes every effort to show people how to help themselves, even when supervisors can't accommodate requested changes quickly.

Nutritionist
A Major Pharmaceutical

Thank you very much for your kindness to send me a complimentary copy of your book. Not only I, but all my colleagues and staff of our Department found this book very interesting and fascinating.

Henry S. R. Kao
Department of Psychology
University of Hong Kong

Thank you for the copy of your book you gave us at NETWORLD. After looking it over, we find that it is too elementary ("Thank you," replies the author) for our readers and we will be unable to distribute it. I am sending the copy back to you. Thank you for your interest in our company, and good luck in your publishing endeavors.

Editorial Assistant
A Professional Book Company